BEHIND HER SCALPEL

A Practical Guide To Oral And Maxillofacial Surgery
With Stories Of Female Surgeons

Authored and Edited by
Cathy Hung, DDS

With Guest Writers:
Rania A. Habib, MD, DDS
Leslie Halpern, MD, DDS, PhD, MPH

And Contributors

Illustrated By:
Victoria Mañón, DDS, MBA

INDIE BOOKS
INTERNATIONAL®

ISBN-13: 978-1-952233-75-3
Library of Congress Control Number: 2021917856

Designed by Joni McPherson

INDIE BOOKS INTERNATIONAL, INC.®
2424 VISTA WAY, SUITE 316
OCEANSIDE, CA 92054

www.indiebooksintl.com

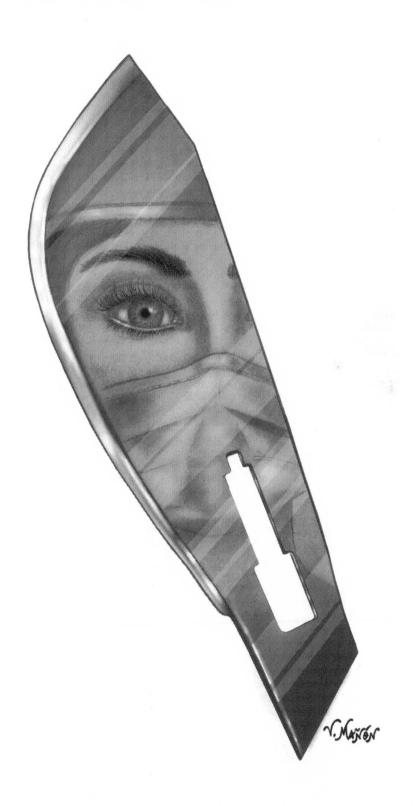

#BehindHerScalpel

"What an amazing compilation of inspiring stories Dr. Hung has put together for us to share in the journey of women through dentistry and surgery! The struggles we all suffer at accomplishing our goals are only more vivid for women and minorities as depicted in this book. A must-read for any woman considering oral surgery as a specialty after dental school."

Dr. Mary Jane Hanlon, Associate Dean of Tufts University School of Dental Medicine
Founder, The Woman in Dentistry Podcast

"As a first-generation immigrant, minority, and academic oral and maxillofacial surgeon, reading this compilation of stories put together by my friend and colleague Dr. Cathy Hung makes me proud to be an OMS! I am as proud and appreciative of the women who contributed to this text. Training to become a surgeon, regardless of race or gender, is already a grueling endeavor. As a minority, female, or both, it becomes that much more of a challenge. This inspirational book puts together so succinctly the trials and tribulations of female oral and maxillofacial surgeons and is a must-read for anyone with an interest in surgery, social sciences, or diversity/inclusion."

Shahid R. Aziz, DMD, MD, FACS, FRCSEd, Assistant Dean, Global Health
Professor, Department of Oral and Maxillofacial Surgery, Rutgers School of Dental Medicine
Associate Professor, Division of Plastic and Reconstructive Surgery, Department of Surgery, Rutgers NJ Medical School
President, New Jersey Society of Oral and Maxillofacial Surgeons

"Dr. Hung has written another bestseller! *Behind Her Scalpel* is a must-read for anyone who is serious about furthering their education and fulfilling lifelong goals. It is inspiring to read about the challenges these women overcame to become the successful individuals they are today. I sincerely enjoyed reading the book. It tells the story of what women really go through to reach success. It has not been given to us on a silver platter. Bravo!"

Julie Bencosme, RDH, MA, CHES Professor of Dental Hygiene-Eugenio Maria De Hostos Community College
President, New York Chapter, Hispanic Dental Association

"It was truly a pleasure to get to know Dr. Hung during her time in the ADA Institute for Diversity in Leadership Program. Dr. Hung's perspective as a first-generation immigrant and a woman makes *Behind Her Scalpel* an inspirational read that provides readers with a look into the unique challenges and opportunities of female oral and maxillofacial surgeons. This book is a must-read for women considering oral and maxillofacial surgery as a career."

Susan Galvan, Senior Manager, Diversity, Equity and Inclusion, American Dental Association

TABLE OF CONTENTS

DEDICATION

*To all the female dentists, physicians, and surgeons
who devote their lives to others every day.*

NOTE

This book adheres to the Chicago Manual of Style.

FOREWORD

T
o be successful, a woman has to be much better at her job than a man," said Golda Meir, and hence, Dr. Cathy Hung's new book, *Behind Her Scalpel*, was born. The book talks about struggles and barriers of female dentists who seek a career as oral maxillofacial surgeons. Dr. Hung delivers a well-thought-out synopsis from struggle and frustration to guidance and mentorship. It is filled with stewardship and hope. The hope that "we need to reshape our own perception of how we view ourselves. We have to step up as women and take the lead," as Beyonce said.

Dr. Hung expresses this desire by moving herself forward, thus advancing and advocating for those around her. She incorporated her time at the ADA Institute on Diversity and Leadership to give specific references as to how this initiative helped her to pen this new book. Similar to her first book, *Pulling Wisdom*, Dr. Hung draws from her family's immigrant background to illustrate previous biases and tendencies in the selection process of female residents.

Dr. Hung invites over twenty-four female oral maxillofacial surgeons to share their stories. Each woman contributes and highlights her own personal strain and endeavor. "The question isn't who is going to let me, it's who is going to stop me," said Ayn Rand. This thought-provoking philosophy is exhibited by each of the contributor's experiences.

Later on, Dr. Hung invites her female surgeon colleagues Dr. Rania A. Habib and Dr. Justine Moe to go over the application process for residency and fellowship programs. This section can be applied to other specialties in medicine and dentistry. It allows the reader to have an outline to improve their chances of acceptance into a residency program.

In the final chapters, Dr. Hung invites Dr. Leslie Halpern to talk about the mentee/mentor relationship. This collaboration further assesses the gender equality issue with sensitivity and purpose. Dr. Halpern states not all mentors are of the same gender, a fact I can attest to from personal experience. "Do not wait for leaders, do it alone, person to person." said Mother Theresa. The person-to-person connection is what mentoring is all about.

Dr. Hung's candid yet compassionate book tells a great story, a story that will surely morph from recollections of other professional women in healthcare and other workplaces. I would therefore recommend this reading to any pre-professional woman, looking for the green light to move ahead. "I never dreamed about success, I worked for it," said Estee Lauder.

Maria Maranga, DDS
Second VP, American Dental Association

ABOUT THE AUTHOR/EDITOR

Dr. Cathy Hung

 Dr. Cathy Hung is a board-certified oral and maxillofacial surgeon and a solo practice owner in New Jersey. She is a native of Taipei, Taiwan and came to the US alone at age of eighteen on a student visa. She earned a BA in psychology with a minor in music from University of California at Berkeley and DDS from Columbia University. She received her oral and maxillofacial surgery training from Lincoln Medical and Mental Center in the Bronx, New York. She is an alumna of American Dental Association's Institute for Diversity in Leadership Program. She is a speaker, writer, and Certified Life Coach (CLC) about cultural competency. Her first book, *Pulling Wisdom: Filling the Gaps in Cross-Cultural Communications for Healthcare providers*, is now available at the ADA Bookstore as a practice management tool. In 2020, she was recognized as one of the "most popular" post bloggers by American Dental Association's *New Dentists Now* blog. She was also recognized by Benco Dental's *Incisal Edge Magazine* as one of the "Women Who Inspire 2020." Outside dentistry, she is a selected member of *Forbes'* Women Forum and Rebecca Minkoff's Female Founders Collective.

Victoria Mañón, DDS, MBA

Instagram@maxillofacial_artist

 My name is Victoria Andrea Mañón, and I'm a current OMFS resident at the University of Texas at Houston. I completed a bachelor of science in neuroscience from Baylor University in 2014, and am a 2018 DDS graduate from the UT School of Dentistry at Houston. I am currently a medical student at the McGovern Medical School and will complete my MBA with an emphasis in healthcare management in May 2021 from West Texas A&M. I'm a Houston-native. I have a wide range of academic and clinical interests, but my favorite subjects include global surgery, craniofacial surgery, implantology, collaborative treatment planning, and dentoalveolar surgery. My hobbies include spending time with my family and friends, art, jogging, singing, and traveling.

I can't remember a time when I didn't enjoy working with my hands; art was really no exception. As a child, I enjoyed drawing, painting, and making jewelry; I also shared these hobbies with my family. Many conversations with my twin brother, Victor, revolved around art, music, or writing; we enjoyed thinking about how to create things and what they might mean to ourselves or other observers. When my cousin, Juan Carlos, would come to visit from Venezuela, we'd spend most of our days drawing and sharing tips we learned over the course of the year. We'd compare pieces we completed separately and share our upcoming plans for future pieces. My parents have always been very supportive as well, offering honest, constructive criticism and purchasing my supplies. After I graduated from high school, I devoted most of my time to my studies. Art, in all of its forms, took a backseat as I was highly driven to get into dental school and subsequently oral surgery residency. It wasn't until I started medical school that I resumed creating artwork.

In dental and medical school, I was exposed to Frank Netter, MD's anatomy illustrations. I am a huge fan of his work, not just because of his attention to detail and style, but also how he was able to incorporate his talent into his medical career to help educate health professionals. Merging art and oral and maxillofacial surgery added a new life to my career. I've learned to look at anatomy and surgical procedures with a different perspective and reinvigorated a lifelong joy. For me, the mindset is the perfect combination of surgery, art, and education. I have found that my own education has been enriched because I approach the subject with the intent of having to explain it to others through an illustration or through writing. Despite the medium, for me, art means communicating something to the observer through a style or personality. While the anatomy illustrations require clarity and precision for educational purposes, the details I try to incorporate into each piece are a part of my own intent and style; I want observers to appreciate the beauty I see when I'm looking at a subject.

As I continue to incorporate medical illustrating into my career, I hope that my skills will continue to improve, and that I'll have more opportunities to share my ideas and work with others. In addition to loving the process of creating, sharing ideas and working with others is another fruit of these projects. Illustrating has created new opportunities for me, and I've gotten to meet new and interesting people. Their ideas and insights have given me new perspectives. I'm excited to see where this career will take me, and how the incorporation of art will augment an already rewarding calling.

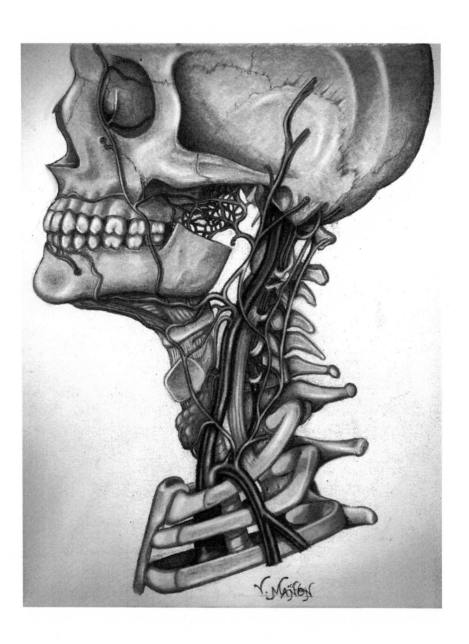

INTRODUCTION

An Open Letter To Present And Future Female Oral And Maxillofacial Surgeons

Congratulations on taking the first step of acquiring this book. Obviously, something about oral and maxillofacial surgery interests you. Perhaps you are a student who is curious about it. Perhaps you have done some research already, or better yet, have gotten interviews with residency programs. Perhaps you are undergoing residency training and wonder what the future might hold after residency. Perhaps you plan to apply for advanced fellowship programs. Or perhaps you have questions or doubts on your mind or simply just need some inspiration. Whichever the case might be, and whatever stage of your schooling or career you are at, I hope you will find at least part, if not all of the book to be relatable, interesting, and helpful in some way. To begin, I would like to give you some background about this book and hope to answer some of the questions about its content.

American Dental Association's Institute for Diversity in Leadership (IDL) Program

This book is a project that resulted from my participation in the Institute of Diversity in Leadership (IDL) program of American Dental Association, Class of 2019–2020. Details about the IDL program can be found on ADA.org:[1]

---

[1] ADA Institute for Diversity in Leadership, ADA.org. American Dental Association. https://www.ada.org/en/education-careers/events/ada-institute-for-diversity-in-leadership, (Accessed May 1, 2021).

The ADA Institute for Diversity in Leadership (IDL) is designed to enhance the leadership skills of dentists who belong to racial, ethnic and/or gender backgrounds that have been traditionally underrepresented in leadership roles.

Since 2003, the IDL program has provided a diverse group of dentists with opportunities to:

- Enhance their leadership skills and gain leadership experience
- Strengthen their professional network and build a lifetime of supportive relationships
- Set new leadership paths within the profession and communities

A Handbook For Aspiring, In-Training, And Practicing Female Oral And Maxillofacial Surgeons

As I was sitting on the short flight from Newark to Chicago in September 2019, in anticipation of meeting with my new class of the Institute for Diversity in Leadership program at the American Dental Association headquarters, a million thoughts went through my mind as to what would be a good project to possibly bring value and benefit future and current dental professionals in the area of diversity and inclusion. Then, it suddenly came to me that my very identity of being a first-generation immigrant from Taiwan who eventually became a female oral and maxillofacial surgeon should be a good start to a project representing diversity within the profession.

I did not come from a family of dentists, physicians, or surgeons. My late father was a chemical engineer-turned corporate executive and my mother was a homemaker with a college degree in accounting and statistics. When I came to the US in 1991 on a student visa, I navigated blindly in the pre-internet era, to stumble upon dentistry, then to finally enter the specialty of oral and maxillofacial surgery—a profession dominated by men and a specialty that remains somewhat of a mystery to the general public. The first time I heard about oral and maxillofacial surgery was during dental school. Had I not had advice from good friends and supportive faculty members to guide me, I wouldn't have thought of applying for oral and maxillofacial surgery, a bridge between dentistry and medicine, a unique specialty that led to a rewarding and fulfilling career. I thought to myself, I must not be the only one who was somewhat clueless and uninformed. When asked, "What do you want to be when you grow up?" it is probably unlikely for a ten-year-old girl to say, "I want to grow up to be an oral and maxillofacial surgeon" unless one of her family members is one.

The gender disparity within the specialty of oral and maxillofacial surgery still remains for several reasons that will be discussed in the book. Across all dental and surgical specialties, the specialty of oral and maxillofacial surgery has the lowest percentage of women.

If my neighbor's seventeen-year-old daughter asked me what oral and maxillofacial surgery is, what would be my thirty-second elevator pitch? What would be my half an hour discussion? What would be yours?

The intent of this book is to inspire young women to understand then pursue the specialty of oral and maxillofacial surgery. It is my hope that it further cultivates female residents and supports practicing female oral and maxillofacial surgeons by providing a rough landscape of the specialty, including information such as the history of how the specialty evolved over time, the scope of practice, how to apply for residency and fellowship programs, women as leaders, and life after residency. The bulk of this book consists of a series of vignettes about female oral and maxillofacial surgeons from different settings—academia and private practices across states and generations—sharing their personal journey. Starting from October 2019, I extended personal invitations to many female oral and maxillofacial surgeons by phone, email, and social media to secure their participation. The surgeons who accepted the invitation filled out a questionnaire I formulated and followed instructions given to provide a personal essay. Due to my own personal time constraints and responsibilities, I regrettably could not include more of you.

I hope this book is just a start and there will be more inspiring stories to be shared in the future.

If you are a young, aspiring surgeon, I hope you feel enlightened after reading this book about the specialty of oral and maxillofacial surgery and are inspired by all the trailblazers who paved the roads for you. I hope this book will help you kickstart your preparation early and equip you with all the knowledge, skills, and tools you need to serve your future. If you are a resident, I hope this book will provide you with strength and positivity when things get tough, as they will, and give you confidence facing the "real world" after residency, especially if you are planning to start a family as a young surgeon. I hope this book serves as a "startup kit" or a scut monkey handbook for you. I hope the challenges surgical specialties possess will not become deterrents—but make you a stronger individual. I hope you will never feel you need to choose between family and career, as the stories in the book will show you can have both.

Female surgeons would like to be known only as "surgeons" and not necessarily to be identified by gender. On the other hand, female surgeons might have unique needs and challenges when it comes to the decisions to start a family, childcare, or simply experiencing different working dynamics with peers and supportive staff members. Intrinsic gender differences do not indicate weakness. A female surgeon should maintain her own authenticity without trying to act like a man to fit in. This book's intent is not to instruct you to play victim or seek special treatment, but to identify where challenges lie and share practical strategies on how to prepare for a successful career. Furthermore, you will read female surgeons' stories of how they have done it, and how you can as well.

At the time of this writing, our nation is still severely impacted by COVID-19. Our dental and medical community has armored up to fight this war. An oral and maxillofacial surgeon is a dentist, physician, and surgeon. We need you to join the force, regardless of age, gender, country of origin, religion, political views, physical build, or skin color.

Disclaimer: I am responsible for the content in this project. Views and opinions expressed herein do not necessarily reflect the positions or policies of the ADA unless such statements have been expressly adopted by the ADA.

What Is Oral And Maxillofacial Surgery?

"Medicines cure diseases, but only doctors can cure patients."

—CARL JUNG

When I was a second-year dental student at Columbia University many moons ago, there was a fair about all dental specialties. Each specialty set a table with pamphlets, brochures, and instruments to showcase what a specialist's future might hold. I distinctly remembered hearing roaring noises from the corner table. I turned my head and saw a group of big guys hovering over a station that displayed, "oral and maxillofacial surgery." I wiggled my way in only to see a spread of extraction instruments and I was quickly body-blocked. My first organic reaction was that I didn't feel I belonged because that was the only table full of men.

However, during the last two years of dental school, my clinical rotation in oral and maxillofacial surgery sparkled something within me. One of the first surgical procedures I saw in the VA clinic was a repair of an oroantral communication, a hole between the mouth and the sinus, as a result of an upper molar extraction. I learned upper molar roots could extend into the maxillary sinus, and dental extraction could potentially cause perforation of the sinus membrane, a thin lining between the mouth and the sinus. Perforation would lead to an opening between the mouth and the sinus. This patient complained that every time he drank coffee, it came out from his nose. During my one month rotation, I witnessed the surgeon close the hole in the maxillary sinus with the aid of a small piece of gold foil, which later led to healing and closing of the area. I was fascinated by the execution of the technique and how the human body responded to a simple elegant maneuver. I was inspired by the magical gold foil. For the last two years of dental school, I explored further into the specialty of oral and maxillofacial surgery, because I was determined to learn more techniques like that to help people resume day-to-day functions most of us take for granted—such as drinking coffee and not having it come out our nose.

What is oral and maxillofacial surgery? The word "maxillofacial" is often confusing and not well understood. Currently, oral and maxillofacial surgery is one of twelve dental specialties recognized by the National Commission on Recognition of Dental Specialties and Certifying Boards (NCRDSCB). Its definition is as follows:

> *"Oral and maxillofacial surgery is the specialty of dentistry which includes the diagnosis, surgical and adjunctive treatment of diseases, injuries and defects involving both the functional and esthetic aspects of the hard and soft tissues of the oral and maxillofacial region." (adopted May 2018)*[2]

Oral Surgeon Or Oral Maxillofacial Surgeon?

Have you been a patient needing an oral surgery procedure? What is your impression of an oral surgeon? One of the most common questions I get from patients is: "What is the difference between an oral surgeon or oral maxillofacial surgeon?"

---

[2] Specialty Definitions. National Commission on Recognition of Dental Specialties and Certifying Boards. ADA.org. NCRDSCB. American Dental Association. https://www.ada.org/en/ncrdscb/dental-specialties/specialty-definitions (accessed May 2021)

Oral and maxillofacial surgery is still a less understood specialty compared to other dental or medical specialties. In a recent study from JOMS by Dalmao et al.[3] investigating the public and professional perceptions of the scope of practice of oral and maxillofacial surgeons, random surveys were sent to the general public, general dentists, and primary care physicians. It was found that more than 25 percent of the general public is unaware of oral and maxillofacial surgery. There was also a low level of awareness among general dentists and primary care practitioners as to the full scope of oral and maxillofacial surgery.

Even the nomenclature of DDS (doctor of dental surgery) versus DMD (doctor of dental medicine) is confusing to the general public. Does the connotation of DDS or DMD have anything to do with the type of specialists? (It doesn't.) Is one better than the other? (They are equivalent.) Most don't understand why some have dental degrees while others have dental and medical degrees. And the abbreviations— OS as in oral surgery, or OMS as opposed to OMFS in reference to oral and maxillofacial surgery—seem to be used interchangeably. To the general public, oral and maxillofacial surgeons are known as dental and medical specialists. Patients may not always understand why they need to visit different dentists for different procedures. Patients also may not understand why we are sometimes called oral surgeons and other times called oral and maxillofacial surgeons. Even dental students or practicing dentists may not all understand the full scope of oral and maxillofacial surgery.

In 1975, the specialty changed its name from "oral surgery" to "oral and maxillofacial surgery." Most people have trouble pronouncing the word "maxillofacial," plus oral and maxillofacial surgeon is not as intuitive or self-explanatory as say, an orthodontist or a dermatologist. Inconsistencies in the names and branding within the profession, often omitting the word "maxillofacial" when communicating with patients,

---

[3] Oscar Dalmao et al., "Public and Professional Perceptions of the Scope of Practice of Oral and Maxillofacial Surgeons." *JOMS* Vol. 79, Jan 2021: Pg. 18-35.

are not uncommon. Ameerally et al.[4] suggested changing the term "oral and maxillofacial surgeon" to "oral and facial surgeon." Some practices use "oral facial surgery" in their name. Guerrero et al.[5] investigated undergraduate students' perception of specialty's name and showed there's an increased awareness among undergraduate students when "oral facial surgeon" was used instead of "oral and maxillofacial surgeon." Interestingly, no difference was found among dental students.

Regardless of the type of training programs, four-year or six-year, we are all called oral and maxillofacial surgeons. Some surgeons choose to practice a full scope of oral and maxillofacial surgery while others prefer a narrower one, naming their practices differently to reflect the procedures performed. There are oral and maxillofacial surgeons who exclusively practice implant dentistry or cosmetic surgery. Many others practice dentoalveolar surgery, or what is considered the "bread and butter" of oral surgical procedures such as surgical extractions and implant surgery with the option of office-based anesthesia. Many surgeons may also hold faculty positions or conduct clinical research in a hospital setting or a teaching institution, or both. One of the advantages of being an oral and maxillofacial surgeon is having a wide array of practice options and flexibility based on area of interest and expertise. You can practice in a private sector, in a university, in a hospital, or a combination of all. Within the scope of practice, you can decide to focus on a few areas or practice a full scope of procedures.

What Does An Oral And Maxillofacial Surgeon Do?

Dental extraction, or exodontia, remains as one of the most common procedures performed in an outpatient setting, with the option to perform outpatient anesthesia. However, oral and

---

[4] P. Ameerally, AM. and Fordyce, IC. Martin, "So you think they know what we do? The public and professional perception of oral and maxillofacial surgery." *Br. J Oral Maxillofac Surg* 32 (1994) 141

[5] AV. Guerrero, A. Altamirano, E Brown, CJ Shin, K Tajik, E. Fu, J. Dean and A. Herford, "What name best represents our specialty? Oral and Maxillofacial surgeon versus oral and facial surgeon." *JOMS* Vol. 75, Issue 1.(2017) P9-20

maxillofacial surgeons are more than "exodontists," a term used in the past.

In 1988, the Second Invitational Conference on OMS (IAOMS) in Bermuda developed a consensus regarding the scope of OMS,[6] which includes:

- Oral pathology/oral medicine
- Dentoalveolar surgery
- Pre-prosthetic surgery (including implantology)
- Surgical and nonsurgical management of TMJ dysfunction
- Facial trauma
- Oncology
- Regional reconstructive surgery
- Orthognathic surgery
- Microsurgery
- Esthetic surgery
- Cleft lip and palate surgery
- Craniofacial surgery
- Others (as technological advances dictate)

Moreover, the *Parameters of Care* was originally developed between 1986 to 1988 by a special committee appointed by the American Association of Oral and Maxillofacial Surgeons (AAOMS) Board of Trustees to address areas of specialty that described patient management strategies, including guidelines, criteria, and parameters. The most recent version of AAOMS ParCare 2017[7] includes eleven areas of oral and maxillofacial surgery:

---

[6] AP.Punjabi and RH. Haug. "The development of the dual-degree controversy in oral and maxillofacial surgery." *JOMS* 48(6) (1990) 621-6

[7] "Parameters of Care: AAOMS Clinical Practice Guidelines for Oral and Maxillofacial Surgery (AAOMS ParCare), Sixth Edition 2017." Supplement to the *Journal of Oral and Maxillofacial Surgery.* JOMS Vol.75 (2017) No.8, Suppl 1.

- Patient assessment
- Anesthesia in outpatient facilities
- Dentoalveolar surgery
- Dental and craniomaxillofacial implant surgery
- Surgical correction of maxillofacial skeletal deformities
- Cleft and craniofacial surgery
- Trauma surgery
- Temporomandibular joint surgery (TMJ)
- Diagnosis and management of pathological conditions
- Reconstructive surgery
- Facial cosmetic surgery

History Of Oral And Maxillofacial Surgery

It would be impossible to understand the specialty of oral and maxillofacial surgery without developing an appreciation for the history of dentistry and oral surgery, the development and evolvement of organizational dentistry and academic programs, and the pioneers who helped to shape and form the specialty to where we are today.

1800 To Early 1900s

During the early 1800s, dental schools did not exist. Most common procedures such as tooth extractions, treatment of dental infections, or treatment of tumors were performed by surgeons who were dentists or physicians, or non-healthcare providers such as barbers or blacksmiths.[8]

The first dental college in the world, Baltimore Dental College, was established in 1840 as a non-university-affiliated dental school, and was the birthplace for the doctor of dental surgery (DDS) degree. Baltimore Dental College later became University of Maryland

---

[8] Leonard B. Kaban and David H. Perrott, "Dual-degree oral and maxillofacial surgery training in the United States: Back to the future" *JOMS*, Vol. 78, Issue 1 (2020)18-28.

School of Dentistry.[9] In 1867, Massachusetts General Hospital and Harvard University opened the first university-affiliated dental school and conferred the doctor of dental medicine (DMD) degree. Dr. Nathan Cooley Keep was the first dean. He popularized the use of ether anesthesia.[10] In 1918, Dr. Menifee Howard invited a group of twenty-nine dentists, or "exodontists," to form the American Association Society of Exodontists, which was then recognized by the National Dental Association in 1919. The National Dental Association became today's American Dental Association.[11]

During this time, there were two especially notable pioneers: Simon P. Hullihen (1810-1857) and James E. Garretson (1825-1895).[12] Hullihen was a physician and the first surgeon in the US to limit his practice to oral and maxillofacial surgery. Garrettson was the first to introduce oral surgery to the Philadelphia Dental College in 1864. Philadelphia Dental College is today's Temple University. He was also the first appointed oral surgery professor in the country. He wrote a textbook in 1869 called *A System of Oral Surgery*.

Wars Accelerated The Need For OMS

World War I and World War II played key roles in the development of oral and maxillofacial surgery. Facial injuries and reconstructions were performed by mostly physicians who held MD degrees, and dentists who volunteered to work in the army.[13] The specialty of plastic surgery did not exist. Deformed faces were covered by masks. Exodontists evolved to perform more extensive oral and facial surgeries during wartime, gradually expanding the scope of practice, which was reflected over time with a name change.

---

[9] University of Maryland, Baltimore. "History." University of Maryland, Baltimore. Accessed May 29, 2021. https://www.dental.umaryland.edu/about/history/.

[10] Leonard B. Kaban and Walter C.Guralnick, "Massachusetts General Hospital/Harvard MD Oral and maxillofacial surgery program." *JOMS* Vol.63. Issue 8 (2005), 1069-72.

[11] AAOMS Centennial. AAOMS History. https://www.aaoms.org/about/aaoms-centennial. (Accessed May 8, 2021).

[12] Daniel Lew. "Chapter 1: Founding A historical overview of the AAOMS". *AAOMS* 2013, Pg. 3,

[13] Danial Lew. *A historical overview of the AAOMS*, Pg. 2.

In 1921, the name of the organization American Association Society of Exodontists was changed to American Society of Oral Surgeons and Exodontists, then later changed to American Society of Oral Surgeons in 1946, and again in 1978 to American Association of Oral and Maxillofacial Surgeons.[14]

During this time, a few key events happened that further facilitated the development and maturation of oral and maxillofacial surgery.

Hospital-Based Dental Services

To perform surgical procedures such as full-mouth extractions, repair of extensive facial trauma or removal of tumors, hospital privileges and presence of dental clinics became necessary. With the discovery of ether anesthesia by Boston dentist William Morton in1846 and penicillin by Alexander Fleming in 1928, more extensive surgical procedures were carried out in the hospital setting.[15] The proposal of dental services in hospital facilities was originally opposed by the medical community. Reasons of objection included lack of academic curriculum, accreditation agency, and professional journal.

Dental Accreditation

In 1936, the American Hospital Association supported dental care in the hospitals. Internship programs began to increase. The Council on Dental Education (CDE) was created in 1949 and the American Dental Association became the accreditation agency. In 1945s annual meeting of the American Society of Oral Surgeons (ASOS), a committee was authorized to conduct examinations for the certification of specialists in oral surgery. The American Board of Oral Surgery (ABOS) was established. The following year, the Board of the American Society of Oral Surgeons was incorporated; its name was changed in 1978 to American Board of Oral and Maxillofacial Surgeons (ABOMS), as it is known today, to reflect the scope of the

---

[14] Daniel Lew. *A historical overview of the AAOMS*. Chapter 1.

[15] Leonard Kaban and David H. Perrott. "Dual degree oral and maxillofacial surgery training in the United States: back to the future." *JOMS* 2020. 78:18-28

specialty. ABOS and ABOMS were incorporated under the laws of the state of Illinois.[16]

First Issue Of The *Journal of Oral Surgery*

In 1942, the Board of Trustees of the American Dental Association voted to publish the *Journal of Oral Surgery*.[17] The first issue was published in 1943. In 1981, the ownership and publication were purchased by the American Association of Oral and Maxillofacial Surgeons, and the following year, the *Journal of Oral Surgery* changed its name to the *Journal of Oral and Maxillofacial Surgery*.

Continuous Evolution And Development Of Training Programs

The initial one-year internship OMS training in the thirties and forties gradually evolved into a mandated three-year program by the American Society of Oral Surgeons in 1967. In 1985, the American Association of Oral and Maxillofacial Surgeons mandated a four-year integrated program, which includes:

- One-year OMS internship
- One year of rotation (three months of medicine, three months of surgery, four months of anesthesia, and two months of an elective)
- Twenty-four months of junior and senior resident level[18]

In 1971, Harvard Medical School developed a five-year integrated oral surgery/MD program. Dr. Walter Guralnick, chief of oral surgery at MGH and Harvard School of Dental Medicine, felt dual-degree training would be necessary to correct the educational deficit present in OMS training programs. He was also an advocate

---

[16] Daniel Lew. *A historical overview of the AAOMS.* Chapter 3. AAOMS.

[17] Daniel Laskin. "The History of the Journal of Oral and Maxillofacial Surgery." *JOMS* 76 (2018): 2046-2050.

[18] Leonard B. Kaban and David H. Perrott: *"Dual-degree Oral and Maxillofacial Surgery Training in the United States: Back to the future."* Pg. 21.

of a full-time faculty training model, as most faculty members in the sixties and seventies were part-time. In 1995, the five-year residency program was expanded into a six-year program under the leadership of Dr. Leonard B. Kaban and Dr. David H. Perrott, with two years of medical school built into it.[19]

From the 1940 through the 1970s, the competition of the overlapping scope of the practice between otolaryngology and plastic surgery presented challenges for OMS in the medical community. Dual-degree programs arguably allow broader scopes of practice and opportunities for advancement to fellowships in head and neck oncology and reconstructive surgery, craniofacial surgery, cosmetic surgery, and other advanced fellowship programs. However, there are many single-degree OMSs who are pioneers and exceptional surgeons practicing full-scope oral and maxillofacial surgery, and their contributions are by no means limited by their single degree. According to the *2019-2020 OMS Program, Resident and Faculty Summary Report,*[20] there are currently one hundred accredited OMS programs—fifty-five single-degree OMS programs and forty-five dual-degree OMS programs—and twenty-three programs that offer both single- and dual-degree tracks. Out of 1,197 residents, 59 percent are enrolled in single-degree programs and 41 percent are in dual-degree programs, plus 19 percent residents are female, an increase from 16 percent in the previous year.

Development Of ACOMS[21]

In 1947, Dr. W. Harry Archer, Dr. Herbert J. Bloom, and Dr. Kurt H. Thoma were three oral surgeons in Boston who initiated conversations of gathering certified oral surgeons to form an

---

[19] Leonard B. Kaban and Walter C. Guralnick. *"Massachusetts General Hospital/Harvard MD Oral and Maxillofacial Surgery Program"*. Pg.1070

[20] "2019-2020 OMS Program, Resident and Faculty Summary Report." *AAOMS*. (Accessed May 2021) https://www.aaoms.org/docs/education_research/edu_training/aaoms_faculty_resident_summary.pdf

[21] "History of ACOMS." American College of Oral and Maxillofacial Surgeons. (Accessed May 2021) https://www.acoms.org/general/custom.asp?page=History

organization to address issues of the American Board of Oral Surgery. Dr. Thoma proposed having a Fellowship of Diplomates of the American Board of Oral Surgeons.

A new organization called the American Diplomates of the American Board of Oral Surgery (ADABOS) received support in 1964, but continued to have challenges and issues. In 1974, the name American College of Oral and Maxillofacial Surgeons was proposed. Its primary objective was to focus on "the upgrading of the quality of the policies and practices of the American Board of Oral Surgery in keeping with the best interests of the specialty." The name was proposed by Dr. Chester Chorazy, and subsequently trademarked.

Today, the American Association of Oral and Maxillofacial Surgeons, American College of Oral and Maxillofacial Surgeons, and American Board of Oral and Maxillofacial Surgeons hold annual conferences and meetings for their members as key organizations for the specialty.

CHAPTER 2

Diversity And Inclusion

Equality. Same. Different.

—THE BRITISH PRIME MINISTER'S OFFICE ON WOMEN

One of American Dental Association's core values is diversity and inclusion. Its 2015–2019 Diversity and Inclusion Plan included three main goals:[22]

1. A diverse membership

2. An inclusive and welcoming environment

3. A system of sustainability

One of my personal favorite quotes about diversity and inclusion was by Verna Myers, the diversity and inclusion expert, attorney, TED speaker, and current VP of Inclusion Strategy at Netflix:

> "Diversity is being invited to the party. Inclusion is being asked to dance."[23]

---

[22] ADA Diversity and Inclusion Statement. American Dental Association. https://www.ada.org/en/about-the-ada/diversity-and-inclusion.

[23] Landing page. VernaMyers.com.

Certainly, those who are invited to the party, but never asked to dance, are still sitting out in the cold. Diversity can exist in any form that is "different from our own"; this includes age, gender, sexual orientation, race, culture, religion, country of origin, language, socioeconomic class, work rank, world views, and so forth. Employing diversity is merely purchasing an entry ticket to the show. Many times, companies may employ diversity due to convenience (there is a need for translation of a certain language) or to fulfill a quota (tokenism). Employing diversity without a desire to understand differences can often lead to conflicts that negate the benefits of diversity: gaining a competitive advantage and bringing in innovative ideas.

Diversity merely indicates the existence of differences. Inclusion is to actively engage individuals and appreciate inputs and opinions different from your own. Inclusion is dynamic and ongoing, especially when there is turnover of your team. If last year's makeup of the residency consists of all men and this year's residency has one woman, the dynamics of the team are bound to change. This woman becomes the "minority" of the group as the "majority" may share more common characteristics. Efforts from the team to make this woman feel included can increase the harmony and work-cohesiveness of the team. A gender-neutral welcome dinner party in a nice restaurant followed by an orientation detailing resident expectations would be a good way to show welcome.

Gender disparity in oral and maxillofacial surgery remains. In my first book, *Pulling Wisdom: filling the gaps in cross-cultural communications for healthcare professionals*,[24] I examined gaps in cross-cultural communication; shared my firsthand experience as a first-generation immigrant doctor; and discussed second language acquisition, the cultural amalgamation process, and strategies to increase diversity and inclusion in the workplace.

---

[24] Cathy Hung. *Pulling Wisdom: filling the gaps in cross-cultural communications for healthcare professionals*. Advantage Books, July 2020.

Half Of The Patients Are Female, But...

According to the 2019 statistics from Association of American Medical Colleges (AAMC) and American Dental Association's 2018–2019 data, medicine and dentistry have coincidentally and concurrently reached 50.5 percent female students entering the first year of medical and dental schools. The 2017 data showed that in general surgery, 40.5 percent of residents in the US were women and 20.6 percent of general surgeons were women. This is a rise from 14 percent female general surgery residents in 2001.[25] [26] [27] However, the statistics about women in oral and maxillofacial surgery remain gloomy. According to the *2019-2020 OMS Program, Resident and Faculty Summary Report,*[28] 19 percent of OMS residents were female, an increase from 16 percent the previous year. With regard to full-time faculty, only 11 percent were female, a 1 percent increase from the previous year—and only 8 percent of AAOMS's members are female. Contrast that to the fact that half the patients we treat are female.

From Tokenism To Tipping Over

Ideally, if 50 percent of surgeons are women, men and women together can bring in different talents and perspectives to achieve higher levels of success from collaboration, rather than segregation or domination. Linda Tarr-Whelan, who served as deputy assistant for Women's Concerns in the Carter administration, ambassador to the U.N. Commission on the Status of Women in the Clinton administration, and chair of the National Advisory Council for the

---

[25] "The majority of US medical students are women, New Data Show." *AAMC.* December 2019. (Accessed May 2021) https://www.aamc.org/news-insights/press-releases/majority-us-medical-students-are-women-new-data-show

[26] "2018-2019 Survey of Dental Education-Report 1: Academic Programs. Enrollment, and Graduates." Health Policy Institute, Commission on Dental Accreditation. (Accessed March 11, 2019) https://www.ada.org/en/science-research/health-policy-institute/dental-statistics/education.

[27] Julia Haskins. "Where are all the women in surgery?" *AAMC.* July 2019, https://www.aamc.org/news-insights/where-are-all-women-surgery

[28] "2019-2020 OMS program, Resident and Faculty Summary Report." *AAOMS.* https://www.aaoms.org/docs/education_research/edu_training/aaoms_faculty_resident_summary.pdf

Pax World Resources Women's Equity Fund, in her book, *Women Lead The Way*,[29] discussed the "30 percent solution." She stated that 30 percent women would be the critical mass, or the tipping point, at which "women's voices resonate fully to add the affirmative difference of our experiences and values" while 50 percent women would be the ultimate goal. She showed evidence that the 30 percent solution would result in better government and business outcomes. She further expressed that "firsts" or "tokens" simply would not have a long-lasting effect.

Before reaching the 30 percent by number, exceptional women surgeons continue to take on leadership roles. The 2015 Summit of Women Oral and Maxillofacial Surgeons led to the first Women OMSs Special Interest Group (SIG) at the 2017 AAOMS annual meeting, led by Dr. Janice Lee. In 2017, Dr. Brett Ferguson became the first African American president of the AAOMS. Dr. Stephanie Drew became the first woman president of ACOMS in 2018. Dr. James Hupp, in his *JOMS* article in 2018, "Our Diversity-Celebrating a Century of the AAOMS," ended with this remark: "I know it is only a matter of time before the AAOMS has its first woman president, helping us further celebrate our association's strengthening through diversity." More recently in *AAOMS Today* January/February 2021 edition, President B.D. Tiner contributed an article titled, "Setting Diversity as a Goal," in which he defined diversity as "recognizing each person is unique and acknowledging our individual differences." Dr. Tinder stated in his Inaugural Address to the House of Delegates in September 2020, that one of the goals is to increase the number of women in OMS residency programs from the current 18 percent to 25 percent in the next three years. He further praised Dr. Debra Sacco, the first female AAOMS trustee member, for her intelligence and enthusiasm, and made the remark "there is no doubt she could end up as the first female AAOMS president." These goals undoubtedly require concerted efforts and support from men and women to achieve them. We need to start by educating our younger

[29]Linda Tarr-Whelan. "Women lead the way". *Fine Communications*, 2009, 2011. Pg. 15.

generations about the specialty of oral and maxillofacial surgery early, maintaining a more harmonious and less-intimidating environment for residents, and creating more leadership programs and roles in diversity and inclusion by doing the following:

Embrace, not tolerate or overemphasize, differences.

Every two years, when I have to renew my Advanced Cardiovascular Life Support (ACLS) certification in a hospital, instructors often ask everyone in the room to introduce themselves. Most of the time, I was the only doctor there in a room of nurses. Because of my gender, I was often assumed to be a nurse, until I introduced myself. Inevitably, there would be occasional dental jokes, comments, or assumptions. I might be put on the spot more, or corrected more, or get a surprised look when I showed I knew how to intubate. The overall experience was benign, but I often felt awkward. Most CPR instructors are not familiar with an oral and maxillofacial surgeon's training and would inquire what I do in my practice. I was often asked why a dentist would need ACLS training.

In a working environment, efforts of hiring and working with diversity may not always translate into inclusion. Michael Slepian, associate professor of leadership and ethics at Columbia Business School, in his *Harvard Business Review* article,[30] pointed out that diversity efforts/ inclusion may fall short because it "does not lead to a sense of belonging" due to "identity-threatening situations." For a survey, he recruited 1,500 individuals of differing identities, including women working in male-dominated fields, LGBTQ individuals, and multiracial individuals, to examine their experiences about identity-threatening situations (being assumed stereotypes, for example), and found an average of eleven of them in a week. He found these identity-threatening situations make

---

[30] Michael Slepian. "Are your D&I efforts helping employees feel that they belong?" *Harvard Business Review.* August 2020. Accessed February 2021. https://hbr.org/2020/08/are-your-di-efforts-helping-employees-feel-like-they-belong

people feel less included and have a negative effect on them. The feelings that these individuals couldn't be themselves—not able to feel authentic—leads to less job satisfaction.

Colorblind Approaches Don't Work

Slepian also pointed out that "it is now clear that a colorblind approach does not effectively manage diversity in the workplace." He stated the problem with colorblind approaches is "a tendency to value homogeny and to seek sameness." A colorblind approach refuses to look at differences by insisting on not looking at colors. However, it is important to examine race and ethnicity as we evaluate diversity and inclusion plans.

When I first came to this country as a freshman in 1991, I studied at Cal State Fresno during my first two years of college. I made friends with two Caucasian, all-American girls, Suzanne and Carla, who lived in my dorm. One day, we decided to go to a Chinese food joint that served spring rolls and fried rice. When we got our order, Carla said to me, "aren't you gonna serve us?" Not knowing what it really meant, I picked up her plate for her. Suzanne, a religious Christian from the South and a genuinely nice person, scolded Carla and told me "you didn't have to serve us at all." Years later, I recalled this event and realized the microaggression and racism I experienced. Carla assumed Chinese people should serve at a restaurant, so I should serve her food like the other Chinese workers. This is an example of an identity-threatening situation. Another example would be a co-resident who was a refugee from Vietnam. He was constantly subjected to "boat people" jokes during training.

Creating A More Inclusive Workplace

In a recent McKinsey & Company survey, one of the factors that has been tested to increase organizational inclusion and diversity is meritocratic company culture,[31] where individuals are advanced

---

[31] P. Bailinson, W. Decherd, D. Ellsworth, and M. Guttman. "Understanding organizational barriers to a more inclusive workplace", June 2020. Survey. McKinsey & Company. Accessed February 2021. https://www.mckinsey.com/business-functions/organization/our-insights/understanding-organizational-barriers-to-a-more-inclusive-workplace

based on abilities and performance. Interestingly, in the survey, less than one-third of women said meritocracy has boosted their careers, while 40 percent of men felt it had. At the same time, research showed women are less likely than men to have substantive interactions with senior leaders. However, meaningful interactions with senior leaders is a factor for career advancement.

Therefore, accepting more women into residency programs is only the first step, but we should not stop there to merely satisfy a quota. The longstanding male-dominated culture must be changed by creating a friendlier, more inviting environment to promote learning and education. The traditional "guys' hangout," which often excludes women, needs to be tossed out, and female residents need to stop being told that they should not be getting married or having children. The misuse and abuse of hierarchical power of the residency based on position must be disallowed and everyone should learn about individual differences rather than making assumptions based on stereotypes. The list goes on and on. The bottom line is, as we are accepting more females in the residency, strategic plans must be formulated to make the training programs more inclusive to keep up with the shifts in group dynamics—instead of expecting female residents to adapt to the norm of the old boys club. We need not to reinvent the wheel. Using corporate diversity and inclusion recommendations as a blueprint would be a good way to start.

Diversity: More Than Race, Ethnicity, And Gender

Racial and gender disparity are most often discussed when it comes to diversity, equity, and inclusion, but there are many areas where disparity can exist. According to the ADA's 2020 data examining leadership seats across the Board of Trustees, Council of Committees, House of Delegates, and New Dentist Committee in terms of leadership diversity, it was found there were 30 percent women, 29 percent new dentists, and only 17 percent minorities.[32]

---

[32] *The changing face of dentistry-meeting the challenge.* A diversity and inclusion toolkit for State and local dental societies. American Dental Association.

It was also found that the majority of dentists in leadership positions are baby boomers, with the exception of millennials occupying the New Dentist Committee. There is a lack of representation from Gen X (1965–85) as leaders. This generational gap accounts for the disparity in leadership diversity in dentistry as a whole.

The next chapter includes a brief account of women pioneers in dentistry and surgery who paved the roads for women oral and maxillofacial surgeons and notes how current statistics reflect the changes in the specialty.

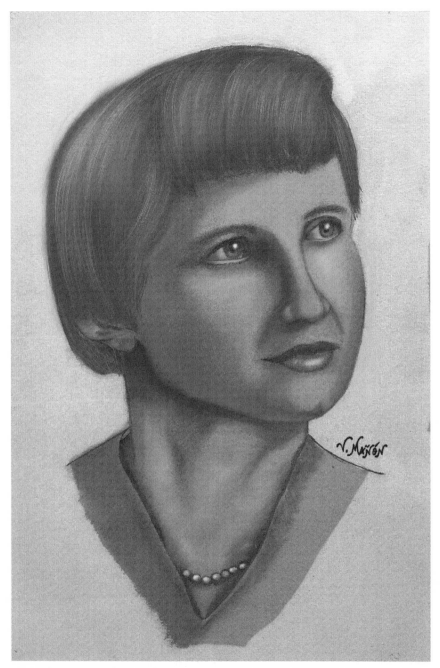

Dr. Elaine Stuebner, the first female graduate from Cook County Hospital oral surgery residency program and the first woman certified as an ABOMS diplomate.

CHAPTER 3

Women In Dentistry And Surgery: A Brief Account

"For our own success to be real, it must contribute to the success of others."

—ELEANOR ROOSEVELT

W hen drinking water, think of its origin." That Chinese idiom describes how we should appreciate those who came before us. As women dentists and surgeons continue to grow within the profession, we cannot help but honor and celebrate the trailblazers who have done it before us to know how far we have come. These women are the "firsts"—the pioneers who refused to conform to the norm, thought outside the box, and worked relentlessly to overcome obstacles, biases, and injustice to elevate themselves and open doors for other women. These women in dentistry and surgery are to be saluted and honored, as they shaped and formed the profession, sprouting diversity knowingly or unknowingly for over more than a century.

Dr. Emeline Roberts Jones (1836–1916)[33] started out being her dentist husband's assistant and was eventually recognized as the

---

[33] *Emeline Roberts Jones.* Connecticut Women Hall of Fame. Accessed March 2021. https://www.cwhf. org/inductees/emeline-roberts-jones.

first woman to practice dentistry in the US, when she joined her husband's practice in 1855. At the time, women were considered "unfit" and dentistry was not for "frail and clumsy fingers" of women. She successfully maintained a career for six decades, even after her husband died, and was inducted into Connecticut Women's Hall of Fame in 1994.

Dr. Lucy Hobbs Taylor (1833–1910)[34] was turned down admission to Eclectic College of Medicine and Ohio College of Dental Surgery because of her gender. She opened a practice at age of twenty-eight to be known as "the woman who pulls teeth" for four years, before proving worthy to be accepted as a member of the Iowa State Dental Society and later be admitted to the senior class of Ohio College of Dental Surgery. She is considered the first woman to graduate from a dental college, in 1866. Today, several organizations honor Dr. Lucy Hobbs Taylor. The American Association of Women Dentists recognizes distinguished individuals with its Lucy Hobbs Taylor Award, and Benco Dental's Lucy Hobbs Project features women who contribute to dentistry each year.

Dr. Ida Gray Nelson Rollins (1867–1953)[35] was the first African American female dentist. She graduated from high school while working part time as a seamstress and in the dental office of Jonathan Taft, who later became the dean of the Dental College at the University of Michigan in Ann Arbor. Taft was supportive of admitting women to dental school and helped Ida to become the first African American woman to graduate with a DDS and the first African American to practice dentistry in Chicago.

Dr. Sara Gdulin Krout (1898–1989),[36] an immigrant who survived the Russian Revolution, graduated from the University

---

[34] *Dr. Lucy Hobbs Taylor, 1833-1910: A Lawrence, Kansas Pioneer in the History of Women in Dentistry.* An Exhibit at the Watkins Community Museum, Lawrence, Kansas. October 2000. Watkins Museum of History. Douglas County Historical Society, Lawrence, Kansas. Accessed March 2021. http://www.watkinsmuseum.org/archives/taylor.shtml

[35] Phylisha W. Agbor. *"Ida Gray Nelson Rollins"*. November 2013. Blackpost.org http://www.blackpast.org/african-american-history/rollins-ida-grey-nelson-1867-1953

[36] Sara Gdulin Krout. Sindecuse Museum of Dentistry, University of Michigan School of Dentistry. https://www.sindecusemuseum.org/sara=gdulin-krout

of Illinois School of Dentistry and was the first woman to serve in the US Navy in 1944. She juggled between work and practice and received the same rank and pay as her male counterparts during her naval service.

Dr. Elaine Alice Stuebner[37] was the first female oral and maxillofacial surgeon. She graduated from the Cook County Hospital residency program in 1958. She also became the first board-certified female oral and maxillofacial surgeon by the American Board of Oral and Maxillofacial Surgeons. She served as the second vice president of the American Dental Society of Anesthesiology, among other achievements. Currently, the American College of Oral and Maxillofacial Surgeons awards Elaine A. Stuebner Scholars annually—outstanding female oral and maxillofacial surgeons.

Surgery and medicine faced similar challenges as dentistry. In the late 1800s and early 1900s, women were generally not considered for formal medical education. Some of the medical colleges were subsequently opened for women but didn't last long.

Dr. Elizabeth Blackwell (1821–1910)[38] was inspired to pursue a medical career due to the loss of a friend to cancer, someone who urged women to "treat the tumors of women." She was rejected by more than twenty medical schools in the US before she was admitted to Geneva Medical College after students voted to allow her admission. However, she could not secure a residency anywhere after medical school. She eventually returned to the US to open the New York Infirmary for Women and Children in 1857. She was the first female physician in the US.

Dr. Kathryn D. Anderson was the first woman president of American College of Surgeons (ACS), elected in 2005. In 2018, ACS for the first time in history had three women holding its highest leadership positions: Dr. Barbara Lee Bass as president, Dr. Leight A.

---

[37] Stephanie Drew. *President's Editorial, Women as Oral and Maxillofacial Surgeons: Past, Present and Future.* July 5, 2018. American College of Oral and Maxillofacial Surgeons. https://www.acoms.org/page/Stuebner/Stuebner-Scholars-Award.htm

[38] Debrah Wirtzfeld. "The History of Women in Surgery". *Can J Surg.* Vol. 52. No.4 August 2009

Neumayer as chair of the board of regents, and Dr. Diana L. Farmer as chair of the board of governors. As of 2018, the ACS's membership was 15.9 percent women.[39]

In organized dentistry, the American Dental Association has had 157 presidents since its founding in 1859. In the ADA's history, there have been four women presidents to date.[40] Dr. Bettie McKaig served from 1998–99 as the first female ADA president, Dr. Kathleen Roth served from 2006–07 as the second, Dr. Maxine Feinberg served from 2014–15 as the third, and Dr. Carol Gomez Summerhays served as the fourth immediately following Dr. Feinberg from 2015–2016. Dr. Kathleen O'Loughlin currently serves as the first female ADA executive director, and Dr. Maria Maranga, an endodontist from New York, currently serves as the second vice president. Examples of other notable women leaders in organized dentistry include Dr. Mary Martin, past president of the American Association of Women Dentists, and Dr. Theresa S. Gonzales, executive director of the American College of Dentists, who is a retired US Army Colonel.[41]

Currently in oral and maxillofacial surgery, there are a number of highly notable female leaders, including Dr. Mary Delsol, the first woman director of the American Board of Oral and Maxillofacial Surgery. Dr. Stephanie Drew became the first female president of the American College of Oral and Maxillofacial Surgery in 2018. In her 2018 president's editorial, there was a comprehensive account on women in surgery and dentistry as well as women leadership. Dr. Suzanne McCormick currently serves as president-elect of ACOMS. She recently created the Women's Leadership Initiative to recruit female oral and maxillofacial surgeons who are speakers. For more information, check out https://www.omswli.com.

---

[39] Diane S. Schneidman. "Women at the helm of the ACS: charting a course to gender equity". *Bulletin of the American College of Surgeons.* September 2018. https://bulletin.facs.org/2018/09/women-at-the-helm-of-the-acs-charting=a-course-to-gender-equity/

[40] *Presidents and History of the ADA.* American Dental Association. https://www.ada.org/en/about-the-ada/ada-history-and-presidents-of-the-ada

[41] Kimber Solana. "Wonder women of dentistry." *ADA News*, April 2019. American Dental Association.https://www.ada.org/en/publications/ada-news/2019-archive/april/wonder-women-of-dentistry

Dr. Debra Sacco is the first woman elected to the board of trustees of the American Association of Oral and Maxillofacial Surgeons. Dr. Janice Lee, the current deputy director at the National Institute of Health's National Institute of Dental and Craniofacial Research, has many "firsts." Dr. Justice Moe of the University of Michigan organized the first, second, and third Annual Women in Oral and Maxillofacial Surgery Symposiums, in 2018, 2019, and 2021, to encourage more female oral and maxillofacial surgeons to network and learn about leadership, mentorship, work-life balance, and other topics crucial to the personal and professional development of female surgeons. Many female dentists and surgeons serve as program directors in dental schools and training programs and hold key positions in translational research as well as clinical care. In this book, my co-contributors will share their stories as leaders and trailblazers—female dentists and surgeons who have dedicated their lives to the greater good of humanity. In the next chapter, these female oral and maxillofacial surgeons share their personal journeys of where they came from and how they achieved their goals against the odds.

The Stories Of Female Oral And Maxillofacial Surgeons

"I do not wish women to have power over men; but over themselves."

—MARY WOLLSTONECRAFT

Pamela Alberto, DMD

- Founder, Cheerful Heart Mission in Haiti and Dominican Republic

- Former assistant dean, Predoctoral Education and Director of Predoctoral Surgery in the Department of OMS, Rutgers School of Dental Medicine

- Alberto and Cho Oral and Maxillofacial Surgery Group; Sparta, New Jersey

A career in dentistry wasn't my lifetime goal. I attended an engineering school, Rensselaer Polytechnic Institute (RPI), where I focused on biology and biomaterials. During a project at the Forsyth Institute, I did research on composites and enjoyed it so much that the dentists who worked with me there suggested I attend dental school. I attended the University of Pennsylvania School of Dental Medicine, becoming one of only thirty-five female dental students in a class of 168. There was only one female faculty member then.

The chairman of OMFS sat me down and told me why I would be a great general dentist since oral surgery was too difficult a profession. I really loved oral surgery and decided to become an oral surgeon. I liked the complexity of it, and the fact that it integrates medicine with dentistry. I realized since there was only one female OMFS in the US, it wasn't going to happen for me. My husband encouraged me to apply. So I did. There was no match then. I saw men in my class with lower class rank get more interviews to residency programs than me. During my interviews, I was told why residency was too hostile for women.

When I applied to the University of Medicine and Dentistry of New Jersey-New Jersey Dental School, I had a different experience with no sexist questions. My interview was normal. There was none of this, "Are you married? If you get pregnant you won't be able to stay in the residency." Dr. Allen Itkin, the chair of the Oral and Maxillofacial Surgery Department, gave me a chance, in part because Dr. Gladys Johnson had paved the way. Gladys was the first African American woman oral and maxillofacial surgeon and my chief resident. I successfully completed my residency, but faced obstacles finding a job. No one wanted to hire women. Dr. Itkin hired me as faculty at New Jersey Dental School. I enjoyed teaching but wanted to include private practice, so I worked for a former resident. We opened a practice together. It was not easy since it was difficult for general dentists to send me patients because I was a woman. They sent me children because they figured kids would be more comfortable with a woman. So I started with children and built my practice. Women have different strengths as oral surgeons. What we do is tough on patients and I find women have more compassion and are willing to listen more to our patients.

In 1989, I became the director of Predoctoral Oral Surgery. After twenty years as predoc director, I was the assistant dean of academic affairs at New Jersey Dental School for two years.

I still enjoy teaching students and residents at Rutgers School of Dental Medicine. I lead an annual dental mission called Cheerful Heart Mission to towns on the border of Haiti and the Dominican Republic, where patients from both nations are treated in two mobile clinics.

The Cheerful Heart Mission after nine years now treats more than 1,000 patients over five days.

My daughter, Catherine Wroclawski, is following in my footsteps, and plans to become an oral surgeon. After receiving her DMD at University of Penn, she will soon begin a six-year residency at the Mayo Clinic.

Although there are now more women in the field, it can still be challenging. Sometimes, patients value women doctors more than our colleagues. But when push comes to shove, the most important thing is how many lives we changed.

Bio

Dr. Pamela Alberto earned her DMD from the University of Pennsylvania, School of Dental Medicine and her specialty certificate in oral and maxillofacial surgery from the University of Medicine and Dentistry of New Jersey—University Hospital. She is a clinical associate professor in the Department of Oral and Maxillofacial Surgery at Rutgers School of Dental Medicine. Formerly, she was the assistant dean of predoctoral education in the office of academic affairs and the director of predoctoral surgery in the Department of Oral and Maxillofacial Surgery. She is a Fellow in the American Association of Oral and Maxillofacial Surgery, the American College of Oral and Maxillofacial Surgery, the Academy of Dentistry International, the International College of Dentistry, and the American College of Dentistry. She is a member of the International Society of Plastics,

Anesthetics and Reconstructive Surgery. She has lectured nationally and internationally on oral surgery, implant surgery, cosmetic surgery, alternative medicine, local anesthesia, and enteral sedation. Dr. Alberto also is the founder of Cheerful Heart Missions, which sends groups of dentists and dental students to Haiti and the Dominican Republic each year to provide oral care to hundreds of patients who would otherwise go without.

Alexandra Bialy, DDS

- US Army Veteran

- Founder, Northwest Society of Women Dentists

- Bialy Center for Oral Surgery, Schaumburg, Illinois

I was born and raised in my beautiful country of Poland and lived there until I turned fifteen years old. It was a communist Poland, not an easy life. We were not well off but happy and never hungry. And then my life suddenly changed. My father, a shipyard worker, decided it was time to leave for a better life. Next, it was three years in Germany waiting for a final destination. Here we come, America! Coming to America, looking at it now thirty-six years later, was the most amazing thing that happened to me next to giving birth to my children. From New York to New Jersey to Chicago, the journey was interesting.

After I learned just enough English, I joined the US Army. After I took my entrance exam, I was told I could pick any job except for intelligence, as my English was not too good. I wanted to be in surgery, as I always loved the medical field since childhood. I was my dolls' doctor, surgeon, and dressmaker. I am really good with my hands. Born as a lefty and forced to use my right hand to write, I have been ambidextrous all my life.

I got the job! After basic training in Fort Jackson in South Carolina, I moved on to medical training in Fort Sam Houston in Texas and my first assignment at Redstone Arsenal in Alabama, and finally to Landstuhl, Germany, where I worked as a surgical technician, a 91D, as my job was described in military language.

It was a great ride and I learned so much. I became an American citizen; got married, divorced, and married again; and had a daughter who is a dentist now. What was most amazing of all is that I finished four years of college while on active duty. In the evenings and weekends, I attended college at a local university that accommodated military personnel. I worked hard; I had to. I was an immigrant wanting to be a doctor. I wanted to be a surgeon like the ones I was assisting every day. I liked helping women, so I was considering OBGYN or orthopedics, and then my direction changed slightly. My college counselor suggested maybe dentistry was an option for me. What!? A dentist!? I wanted to be a physician! I did fine on my DAT. After my honorable discharge, I found myself back in the Chicago suburbs starting a new life after the army. I got a job at a local hospital as a surgical technician and applied to dental schools. Oh well, I can be a dentist. I found myself next to oral surgeons, watching them work in the mouth, and then I realized oral surgery was my future! I could be a surgeon of the mouth! And that was my goal, to become an oral surgeon; little did I know that it was not going to be an easy path to get there.

I did well in dental school; I actually fell in love with the oral cavity and everything else that went along with it. I applied to several residencies and matched at the University of Illinois at Chicago. I needed to be close to home for support. My now ex-husband was not interested in my career and gave me a choice: either get a job as a dentist or leave. So, I packed my bags and left with my seven-year-old daughter, moving to Chicago to start my residency. I owe a huge thanks to my mom, who moved in with me to take care of my child when I was gone days at a time, and to my dad, for letting my mom live with me.

Residency was hard. I was a single mom going through a divorce. But I loved what I was learning and doing! I didn't care about male dominance. I could handle guys; I'd just spent seven years in the US Army, so I knew how to deal with them. I didn't care if that was the most challenging project of my life, maybe after getting divorced.

I wanted to be an oral surgeon. I loved it, I loved the challenges, the patients, and my future was bright!

I graduated and worked for a group of oral surgeons. I was an associate for two years for a group of male oral surgeons, and I realized that as a female oral surgeon, things were different for me. Male oral surgeons might have wives who take care of them, their kids, their home, and their laundry and cooking. I wanted a different lifestyle, a lifestyle that would allow me to be a woman, a mom, a business owner, a decision-maker, and a queen oral surgeon. I did learn a lot from my first job. I am thankful for that experience.

Three months before I opened my own oral surgery practice, I had my son. Now he is a teenager who is looking into a military career like his mom. I have been a solo oral surgeon in the suburbs of Chicago for almost sixteen years. I love the rewards and challenges of being a woman oral surgeon, a business owner, a mother, and a yogi. I try to learn new techniques, new approaches, new ways, and new yoga poses. I love my staff, I treat them well, I pay them well, and we talk about being strong women. We have no men working in my practice—it is a fully female staffed business—and we focus on making ourselves stronger and better.

I believe we women can do anything we set our mind to doing. We women can be oral surgeons and women are now in combat. Why is it that people wonder about women wanting to do what men do? And who decided that it makes a difference if you are a woman or a man when something has to be done?

It is our time, ladies! Let us make our daughters strong, and our sons confident in their women. Ladies, it all starts at home, with us, believing our daughters are capable of anything.

Bio

Dr. Bialy is originally from Poland. She is an owner of Bialy Center for Oral Surgery in Schaumburg, Illinois. She received her bachelor's degree in biology from the University of Alabama while serving on active duty in the US Army. She achieved the rank of staff sergeant. She also earned her bachelor's degree in dentistry and DDS from the

University of Illinois at Chicago. Her residency in oral and maxillofacial surgery was completed at the University of Illinois at Chicago, where she was the chief resident on staff with several affiliations, including West Side Veterans Administrations Hospital, Cook County Hospital, Mercy Hospital, London Health Sciences Centre, and St. Thomas Elgin General Hospital in Canada.

Dr. Bialy is a member of the American Association of Oral and Maxillofacial Surgeons and Illinois Society of Oral and Maxillofacial Surgeons. She is a founder of the Northwest Society of Women Dentists.

Donita Dyalram, DDS, MD, FACS

- Associate professor, Program director, OMFS Residency, University of Maryland

- Associate program director, Oral-head and neck surgery/microvascular surgery Department of OMS, University of Maryland dental school

- Faculty Educator Development Award from the Oral Maxillofacial Surgery Foundation

- Examiner of American Board of Oral and Maxillofacial Surgery

My journey to becoming an oral maxillofacial surgeon did not begin on a clear path. It was not filled with altruistic desires but was rather a pragmatic decision. I went to dental school so I could learn a skill and always be guaranteed a means to earn a decent living—a living that would ensure enough financial security to help myself and my parents have a comfortable life. We were immigrants from South America, and I grew up seeing my very educated parents work arduously in jobs that did not use their potential just to survive in New York City to give their children a better opportunity in life.

Dental school was the choice I made after speaking to friends in undergraduate college. They spoke of their parents' jobs as dentists, and I saw how their lives were enriched. Also, they were on their way to a career in dentistry. Thus, the career path of dentistry fulfilled the requirement for a stable future. While in dental school, I rotated through the different specialties of dentistry: pediatric dentistry, prosthodontics, oral maxillofacial surgery, orthodontics, and periodontics. Of all these great possibilities, oral surgery was the most fascinating and intriguing. I can still remember the first tooth I extracted in the oral surgery clinic. The thrill, the instant gratification, and the thanks from the patient could not make for a more rewarding experience. Little did I know at that time what it meant to be an oral maxillofacial surgeon or the vast scope of such a practice. But I was hooked, and it was the start of my journey to becoming an oral maxillofacial surgeon.

I did the usual things a student interested in oral surgery would do when considering a career path: volunteer in an oral surgery practice, spend every free moment in the school's clinic, extern at numerous programs, and speak to the residents and faculty. At the end of this search, I realized I indeed wanted to be part of this remarkable profession. I matched into an MD-integrated OMFS program. It must have been as if I looked through a crystal ball, because without being part of the dual degree program, I would not have been able to accomplish the things I have today.

Residency is residency. I tried to find my place, get over the shell shock of the hospital system, and learn to manage diseases and treat patients. I grew up in residency. During this time, I met a few people whose influence in my education led me to where I am today.

My chief resident when I was an intern was one of those people. He was tough, he was demanding, he had high standards, and most of all he was fair. Dr. Shawn McClure is now a head and neck surgeon at Nova University. At the time, I did not even have an inkling that our paths would cross again. As the years passed during residency, I looked back at general surgery with fondness and recalled the challenges and joy I had treating patients. And, as I commenced my senior year of training, the thought of what type of surgeon I wanted to become weighed heavily on my mind.

The recurring theme was I wanted to be the best surgeon to my patients and one who could handle any situation that arose. I wanted to fill my toolbox of skills with everything attainable. During my training days, there were few OMFS programs with oncology- and microvascular-trained surgeons. My residency program, SUNY Downstate/Kings County Hospital, was such a program. I began pursuing a path that would make me a head and neck oncology and microvascular reconstructive surgeon to fill my toolbox of skills.

I interviewed at the University of Maryland OMFS Oncology and Microvascular Fellowship Program. There, I met two people who shaped my future and who I credit for my place in the world of surgery today. Dr. Joshua Lubek was my fellowship director and trained me to be a microvascular surgeon. Dr. Robert Ord taught me ablative oncologic techniques. Together, these two prolific individuals made me a head and neck/microvascular surgeon.

My fellowship days were not easy to say the least. Long days, longer nights, memorable patients who I still see today, and those I miss who succumbed to their disease. I still remember morning coffee and weekend life lesson discussions with Dr. Ord. I fondly nicknamed them "Weekends with Bob." I consider Dr. Ord my mentor and my teacher to this very day, and Dr. Lubek's energetic personality, demanding work ethic, and mastery of microsurgery made for outstanding fellowship training. Today, I have the pleasure of calling these two individuals colleagues and dear friends.

I chose to become an academic surgeon after fellowship and was granted this opportunity at the University of Maryland. I am fortunate to work with outstanding leaders in oral maxillofacial surgery each day and to have a career I love in a place I love. As a dental school faculty member, I can teach and mentor many students who have a keen interest in OMFS. Through the OMFS student interest group, I helped realize this dream in many of our students.

It is troubling when women make up 50 percent of dental school classes and it does not translate to the oral surgery profession. As a faculty member, it is exciting when I see a female dental student thrilled about being in the operating room and wanting to know more about OMFS. I can't wait to tell her that she, too, can have it all: be an oral surgeon, be a mentor, be a leader, be a role model, and be a mom. Although the road there may be tough and long, it is achievable and equally as rewarding.

Being the program director of the Maryland OMFS residency program gives me the ability to help train future surgeons. To see a young intern mature to a competent surgeon could not make me prouder. What a great pleasure and honor this is to have such an influence in their lives and help them achieve their dreams as others helped me achieve mine.

As an academic head and neck/microvascular surgeon, I have had the opportunity to train future leaders in this field as well. I have trained several fellows who are making their mark in the world. This career path has given me the rare and unique opportunity to be on the face transplant team at the University of Maryland Medical Center.

The mission of the Maryland training program is to train citizen surgeons. It is a mission the faculty and residents take to heart. I have helped organize oral cancer screenings and walks for awareness of oral cancer. I am doing my due diligence in conducting research in this field. I am also doing my part in exposing high school students to dentistry and teaching them about oral cancer.

Treating cancer patients, whether it is removing their tumor or rebuilding their tongue, cheek, jaws, or throat, can be a humbling experience. To see them through their darkest hour, I cannot help but form a bond with them. I have come to see my patients over the past four years in practice survive and some who fought like champs but lost the battle.

I did not become a cancer surgeon because I wanted to fight cancer. I became a cancer surgeon to be a competent surgeon and, in the end, I became a surgeon who wants to eradicate cancer.

I look back at my journey and it appears almost serendipitous that all the roads led me to this point. I now look ahead with excitement to see where this journey leads.

Bio

Dr. Dyalram is currently the program director in the Department of Oral and Maxillofacial Surgery at the University of Maryland Medical Center. She attended New York University College of Arts and Science for her undergraduate degree. She then obtained her dental degree from New York University College of Dentistry and her medical degree from SUNY Downstate Medical Center. At the completion of oral maxillofacial surgical residency training at SUNY Downstate Medical Center/Kings County Hospital Center in New York City, she left her home to pursue fellowship training in head and neck oncology and microvascular reconstruction at the University of Maryland Medical Center. Following two years of fellowship training, she accepted an academic position at the University of Maryland Medical Center, Department of Oral Maxillofacial Surgery.

Since this time, she has remained at the University of Maryland and she is currently the program director of the OMFS residency training program. She is also the associate fellowship director of the head and neck oncology/microvascular reconstruction fellowship training program, through which she trains two fellows in ablative techniques and microvascular reconstruction each year. She is also course director and faculty advisor to students at the University of Maryland Dental School.

Dr. Dyalram was awarded the prestigious Faculty Educator Development Award by the Oral Maxillofacial Surgery Foundation. This reflects her commitment as an educator to students, residents, and fellows. She is board certified by the American Board of Oral & Maxillofacial Surgery and is currently a junior ABOMS examiner. She is a member of the face transplant team at the University of Maryland Medical Center.

Dr. Dyalram maintains a clinical interest in tumors of the jaw, benign and malignant; squamous cell carcinoma of the head and neck, salivary gland tumors, sialendoscopy osteoradionecrosis and medication-related osteonecrosis of the jaw, head and neck reconstruction, trauma, and trigeminal nerve repair.

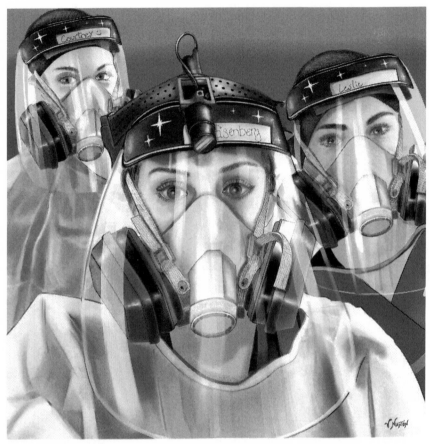

Dr. Nicole Eisenberg with her team members wearing 3M respirators with P100 cartridges and face shields during COVID-19 to treat patients.

Nicole Eisenberg, DDS

- TEDx speaker, Boston Marathon athlete, and former US Navy commander

- Knoxville Center for Oral and Maxillofacial Surgery

- Affiliated with the University of Tennessee Medical Center Knoxville (UTMCK) and East Tennessee Children's Hospital (ETCH)

The road that led me to oral and maxillofacial surgery was direct. I grew up in a home surrounded by dentistry; my father is an endodontist, and my mother helped run his office. I spent many hours playing in his office and then assisting during school breaks. I was drawn to science in school and enjoyed chemistry, AP biology, and especially the lab experiments. When I started Samford University on a track & field scholarship, I wanted to pursue physical therapy because of my interest in sports and medicine. During Christmas, my sophomore year of college, I spent the break working in my dad's office and observed two oral surgeons working in the same office complex. I was intrigued that they performed anesthesia and surgery, that they had the ability to remove fear and anxiety by sedation and then perform complex surgery. I also took a tour of the dental school in Memphis and was able to meet with several faculty and students as well as observe a class working on patients.

I returned to college with a strong interest in oral surgery and a decision to pursue dental school. Luckily, I did not have to alter my course schedule too much because of the overlap with prerequisites. When I was home from college on breaks, I spent time with my father and his oral surgeon friends, observing and assisting. Firmly on my path to dental school, I applied for and was accepted into a Navy scholarship (HPSP), where they sent me to dental school in return for a term of service required after graduation.

I started dental school immediately after graduating college. During Christmas break of my first year, I assisted a local oral surgeon with an orthognathic case, and I was hooked. I knew I was interested in oral surgery from observing office procedures, but I was astonished watching the oral surgeon down-fracture the maxilla and was sold when I was allowed to place a screw into one of the plates. He and the oral surgery residents cautioned me before they down-fractured the maxilla, saying a lot of people get nauseated. They laughed when I exclaimed, "That is the coolest thing I've ever seen!" The oral surgeon included me in the dictated operative note, and I keep it in a special folder as my first oral and maxillofacial surgery case.

I started my second semester of dental school determined to continue to make the best grades possible and learn more about the application process for oral surgery. Once we moved into clinical rotations, I spent my extra time with the oral surgery department and learned more about oral surgery residencies. I spent time with the residents and asked to take calls to learn more. My male classmates could take calls, as it was up to the on-call resident, but I was not allowed. The all-male oral surgery residents said they did not feel comfortable sharing spaces and having me, a woman, around. It was the first time the male-dominated profession I chose to pursue directly revealed its sexist ways.

Undeterred, the summer between my third and fourth year, I did an externship at Naval Hospital Balboa in San Diego with the oral surgery department. I learned what it meant to be an oral surgery resident; it meant *living* at the hospital, being available at all hours, and learning an immense amount of material in a short period of time. I assisted in cases at all hours, I learned to suture lacerations in the ER, I watched the interactions between the residents and staff, I listened to the conversations with the patients, and I decided emphatically that I wanted to be an oral and maxillofacial surgeon. I decided four more years of schooling, time away from family and friends, and delaying personal milestones such as marriage and children was worth it because I knew I would not be happy as a general dentist. I was not married at the time but was in a long-distance relationship with a man serving in the US Navy. He spent a month with me during my externship at Balboa Hospital and was able to see some of the lifestyle I was wanting to pursue. We had a serious discussion about the intense pathway and road to becoming an oral surgeon and agreed to continue our relationship; I would look for OMS programs that were close to Navy bases where he could potentially work.

I started my fourth year of dental school determined to pursue oral and maxillofacial surgery and finally had the courage to say it out loud and tell my classmates. Although there were mixed reactions, most were shocked and unsupportive. I had support from my family and a handful of friends, although most female friends thought I was insane for choosing such a demanding and male-dominated path. My male classmates openly expressed their thoughts that I was not tough enough. The most disheartening response was from the nearly all male oral and maxillofacial surgery teaching staff, which did not even take my desire seriously and refused to help.

Undaunted, I completed the application process and was offered multiple interviews. Invitations for interviews arrived at different times and some programs had interviews on the same day. For example, I was offered an interview at one program, and I accepted, only to be offered an interview at another program on the same day. I did not think it was professional to cancel an interview I had already accepted, so I was unable to interview at some programs. I attended interviews at six oral and maxillofacial surgery programs, with most programs only interviewing one to two other women as compared to dozens of men. One program specifically told me my interview was just to fill a quota, to show on paper that they had interviewed a woman. They had no intention of accepting a female applicant. Another program had a night out with interviewees and the residents. I was the only female present and one of the senior residents told me if I spent the night with him, he would get me into the program.

I completed my final application list with locations close to naval bases in mind rather than where I felt I would fit in best. Looking back, this was probably not the best decision for training purposes, as there were better oral and maxillofacial surgery programs that would have been suited to my personality or had other women as residents and faculty, but I was committed to making my relationship *and* my career in oral and maxillofacial surgery work.

I received a call early the morning of match day from the oral and maxillofacial surgery program director welcoming me to the program at Hospital of Saint Raphael with Yale School of Medicine. My world changed in an instant. In five months, I would be moving from Memphis, Tennessee to New Haven, Connecticut. After my match, my boyfriend sought and was able to receive orders to Naval Station Groton, only thirty minutes away from New Haven. He, too, sacrificed more professionally rewarding opportunities elsewhere to ensure we could be together. We decided to live together and found a rental home about halfway between our soon-to-be new workplaces. The day I graduated from dental school, he proposed to me (I said yes!), so we moved to Connecticut and I began my oral and maxillofacial surgery residency.

Why do I enjoy being an oral and maxillofacial surgeon? I fell in love with the unique combination of anesthesia with surgery and the diverse scope of practice. It was never about the amount of money I could make; it would have been easy to pursue endodontics like my father and cash in on his established client base. The lifestyle seemed stressful rather than glorified, but I was willing to accept the stressful lifestyle to have a life doing what I enjoy.

Since becoming an oral and maxillofacial surgeon, I still enjoy the "bread and butter" aspects of oral surgery. I enjoy sedating patients, removing teeth, and the mental puzzle of some cases—like figuring out the best way to section and remove an impacted lower third molar, the differential diagnosis of an unusual oral lesion, and the artistry of cosmetics like Juvéderm. Moreover, I love that after practicing for almost fifteen years, I am still learning new things and perfecting my techniques. It is a lifetime of learning and growing to be the best for my patients. I enjoy the wide diversity of oral and maxillofacial surgery; it encompasses so many areas, from anesthesia, dentoalveolar, trauma, cosmetic, pathology, pain management, and reconstruction to medicine and dentistry. The scope of practice is so extensive.

I am the first female oral and maxillofacial surgeon who came into my community and I am actively trying to break into the good old boys network in a traditional Southern community. I moved to the community recently and I did not complete my training in the area, so I am considered an "outsider." The push in oral surgery is to call yourself an "oral surgeon" not a "female oral surgeon," but the community I work in only knows of an oral surgeon as a male. It is challenging to adapt into an environment that is resistant to change. My story is one of several, but I have teamed up with TIME'S UP Healthcare to break the stereotypes, end the discrimination, and stop sexual harassment and assault. I completed the 2019 New York City Marathon representing TIME'S UP and connected with some phenomenal women who have become mentors during this journey. I worked with University of Tennessee students and the Title IX office and had the opportunity to share my story, "Breaking Down Barriers in Healthcare, The Need for More Women in Surgical Specialties," on February 13, 2020, at the TEDxUTK: Opening The Door event.

After years of not knowing how to effectively fight against the discrimination and harassment, I am trying a different approach. Instead of just reporting the incidents, I am trying to change the environment. I am helping other women by mentoring, advising, and leading as an example of what needs to be done. I have given lectures to the oral and maxillofacial surgery residents and shared my TEDxUTK talk. I am not afraid of the retribution for speaking out, as I now own my oral and maxillofacial surgery practice, so I am not worried about the retaliation I have faced in the past. I have a great core group of supporters and they are helping me stand strong. My own practice is running based on the way I feel people need to be treated, my employees and my patients, and it feels good to do what is right, not what makes the most money.

What have I learned on my journey? What would I tell others as they contemplate their path? Be fierce. Stay strong. Treat others the way they deserve to be treated, not how you were treated. Trust but verify. Anticipate, anticipate, anticipate! Always tell the truth. When you make a mistake, own it, learn from it, and move on. Do not lose yourself in the process, keep your humanity.

Realize that not everyone has your best interest in mind. At the same time, do not put up a wall; let people in and get help when you need it. Learn from others, do not assume you know everything. You must be confident but not arrogant. Find a successful female mentor. It is great if they are a surgeon as well, but any strong and wise woman can help. You will need a "cheerleader" who can help build you up when you are torn down and will not give up on you when things get tough.

Do not put up a wall; let people in and get help when you need it.

Bio

Dr. Nicole Eisenberg grew up in Memphis, Tennessee and attended Briarcrest Christian School. She received her BS in exercise physiology from Samford University, Birmingham, Alabama in 1999 and earned her DDS from The University of Tennessee, Memphis in 2003 under the Armed Forces Health Profession Scholarship Program. She then completed her residency in oral and maxillofacial surgery at the Yale-New Haven Hospital/St. Raphael campus in 2007.

Dr. Eisenberg completed nine years of service as a commander in the US Navy in July 2016 and moved to Knoxville, Tennessee. While in the Navy, she served in various surgery and staff positions in Norfolk, Virginia; San Diego, California; Okinawa, Japan; and Washington, DC.

Dr. Eisenberg is Board Certified by the American Board of Oral and Maxillofacial Surgery and National Dental Board of Anesthesiology. She is a member of several professional organizations, including the American Dental Association, American Association of Oral and Maxillofacial Surgeons, American College of Oral and Maxillofacial Surgery, American Dental Society of Anesthesiology, Tennessee Dental Association, and Tennessee Society of Oral & Maxillofacial Surgeons.

Dr. Eisenberg opened her own practice, Knoxville Center for Oral & Maxillofacial Surgery, in January 2019. She practices the full scope of oral surgery and covers trauma calls at East Tennessee Children's Hospital.

Dr. Eisenberg is an avid member of the Knoxville running community and has qualified to run the Boston Marathon twice. Her husband, Mitch, is a US Naval Academy graduate who retired from the Navy in April 2020 and currently is an assistant district attorney with the Office of the District Attorney General of Knox County. Mitch and Nicole have boy and girl twins that keep them busy with numerous activities.

Bridget Ferguson, DDS

- Oral and maxillofacial surgeon, Veterans Hospital, Orlando

- Former clinical director, OMS Clinic, Columbia University College of Dental Medicine

- ADEA Emerging Leaders Program

- US Navy Veteran

- Recipient, 2018 Edward V. Zegarelli Teaching Award and Columbia University CDM Henry Sage Dunning Award

Most of us do not start our career search in junior high with an inherent genius or passion to become dentists or oral surgeons. I never even considered pursuing science or healthcare until high school. To me, a potential career path evolves over time with a variety of ongoing experiences stimulating curiosity and more learning. It is a winding path of challenges that may occasionally verge on overload. And, at the "end" of the garden path, you may find the road keeps extending, leading to more variety, and this cycle keeps life interesting. Even if you have not taken the exact journey as I have—training through school and the military, then on to private practice and academia—the professional quest is one that involves finding a balance. It is a combination of self-discovery fueled by mentorship.

Taking the Plunge

As I was heading into high school, I had assumed I would be an accountant. My whole family before me had taken the business route. So, I enrolled in all the business classes my high school offered. This was going just fine until my junior year of high school's mandatory biology class.

My high school biology course was fueled by an amazing teacher, who, now that I look back, provided a turning point in my career. Studying the rhythms of life itself showed me a world of fascinating subject areas—ones I could both encounter concretely but also feel were always new, unfolding just a little beyond my initial reach—in contrast with the mundane debits and credits of accounting. My teacher was so influential for me that I decided to take her next course, advanced biology. That sealed the deal. None of my business classes gave me the same excitement and interest as the biology courses. I decided then that I wanted to go to medical school.

My college life was great. I studied hard but knew very early on that the pressure and competition to get into medical school was more than I could handle, and it would be beneficial to explore other healthcare options. Dental school occurred first to me because I loved my dentist and the profession appeared on the surface to entail a balanced and nice quality of life. I was fortunate enough to be on the collegiate tennis team throughout my years in school and always had strove to find that work-life balance. I always wondered if I could do so in the professional world. I entered dental school sometimes wishing I was actually in medical school but pushed ahead mainly due to my Navy scholarship pressures to complete graduation.

Getting My "Sea Legs"

I applied and was accepted for a full ride scholarship to join the Navy after completing dental school. I never planned on specializing in dental school; oral pathology did cross my mind, bringing back my love for basic sciences. Dental school had been very tough for me; I was unsure where my path would take me after learning the basics of the craft. I had been used to more certainty. I confess that newness-feeling created anxiety, or maybe it was a lack of confidence, but I kept going.

I had entered the Navy as a general dentist. But one thing happened unexpectedly—something truly beyond my initial reach, a challenge I had not anticipated but one that came with a promising reward. One thing I wanted more than anything was to travel and travel a lot. The only way to accomplish this passion was to deploy.

I volunteered to deploy in any capacity, even moving from a Navy status to a Marine Corps status. I was then selected to go on a six-month tour with the Marines around east Asia. But I was lacking one important experience: surgery skills that I didn't have from dental school. In fact, I shied away from surgery in dental school because it appeared initially to be too hard and entail too much time commitment, stress, and pressure. Yet the Navy insisted I must get oral surgery experience. And that is what I did. I basically did oral surgery cases full time until I deployed and started gaining confidence and experience as the days went by.

Taking Flight

After my tour in Okinawa, I was transferred to a yearlong training in general dentistry. As luck would have it, my first rotation was oral surgery. Now equipped with the repetition and confidence of having already focused on that area, I did very well and the oral surgeons took note of it immediately. They encouraged me to apply for formal training in the Navy. That mentorship was a big asset. Honestly, without the oral surgeons taking notice of me, I never would have considered this path for myself. I enjoyed doing oral surgery but never gave it much thought until it was brought to my attention. Here I had thought my next step was going to be simply planning for my next career in private practice with a touch more cosmetic and restorative experience. Instead, a new door had opened. This is one of the reasons mentorship is so important and finding students who are capable and enjoy surgery.

My residency was a different scenario. Receiving mentorship took a back seat to a grind. It was definitely the hardest work experience I have ever encountered. I was also the only female resident in my program and in the end was the first female resident to graduate from the program. I knew ahead of time what I was going into and was not surprised, but this didn't make it any easier. Experience is the best teacher. I benefited from the program director of the residency also being female. At this point, I was off to the aircraft carrier for the next two years.

Working on an aircraft carrier is not for everyone, but it certainly contains that sealed ecosystem that is conducive to honing one's skills. The years following my time on the carrier were packed with studying for boards, gaining more experience at my next naval duty station, and deciding what to do after the Navy. There are many options I considered, including private practice and full-time faculty.

Building Alliances

I was fortunate enough to obtain a position in private practice that included volunteer time in a teaching hospital—which luckily later became my full-time job. Private practice definitely has its share of benefits over full-time faculty academic positions at a residency or dental school. You may be able to make your own hours part time versus full time; take minimal or no call; and earn income that can potentially continue to grow depending on production and type of practice. However, for me, after three and a half years of private practice, I knew it was time to make a change. Academics and teaching had become my passion and purpose. I love working with residents and students. Their energy and vigor to learn is contagious. Even when I am exhausted and don't feel like I can keep going, they bring me up and even have me crying with laughter. They are very intelligent and are constantly learning and it's a pleasure to work with them.

The challenges of any career are that it can put a burden on family and friends and it can feel like a full-time occupation to build limits and boundaries. Academics affords you many opportunities, meaning many more work commitments, including patient care, call, and leadership and administrative duties. I have been a faculty member now for over four years and have selected opportunities that align with my best abilities and purpose.

I have mentored many dental students and residents, spoken at leading conferences and CE courses, and recently was selected for a one-year leadership institute with ADEA. Further advancement in academics could include increasing your faculty practice, building a research project, teaching nationally or internationally, being a vital member of committees in your medical complex, and other dental school obligations that provide you with great networking tools. There are many other opportunities that open up that are not on your immediate radar, like government and senior administration or becoming a dean.

I highly encourage strong mentorship now to enable more women to take the plunge and pursue a career in oral and maxillofacial surgery. I look back on my career path and realize I never knew this was how it would turn out. I encourage women to speak to many mentors in all aspects of oral surgery and be open to the possibilities.

Bio

Dr. Bridget Ferguson was an assistant clinical professor in the Department of Oral and Maxillofacial Surgery at Columbia University College of Dental Medicine. She received her DDS from the University of Minnesota School of Dentistry in 1999 and completed her oral and maxillofacial surgery residency at the Naval Medical Center San Diego in 2008. She is a diplomate of the American Board of Oral and Maxillofacial Surgery.

Dr. Ferguson was the clinic director of the Oral and Maxillofacial Surgery Clinic. She was the course director for the second-year Introduction to Oral and Maxillofacial Surgery series and taught other didactic courses for the third-year oral surgery course, local anesthesia and facial pain management, as well as anesthesia simulation for the oral maxillofacial surgery residents. Dr. Ferguson has received a number of awards for her teaching, including the 2018 Edward V. Zegarelli Teaching Award for dedicated and inspired teaching of dental students and the Columbia University College of Dental Medicine Henry Sage Dunning Award in June 2017 and June 2019.

In July 2016, Dr. Ferguson was nominated to participate at the

Emerging Leaders Program through ADEA and was recently selected as secretary for the section on Oral Surgery/Anesthesia/Hospital Dentistry. She was serving as chair of the Pharmacy and Biomedical Materials Committee. Along with her teaching and commitments, Dr. Ferguson maintained a busy clinical and faculty practice at CDM, which focused on outpatient dentoalveolar surgery, bone grafting, outpatient sedations, trauma, and infections.

Dr. Ferguson moved to Florida with her family in May 2021 to continue her career at the Veterans Hospital in Orlando as a full-time oral and maxillofacial surgeon.

Elda Fisher, DMD, MD, FACS

- Residency program director, University of North Carolina

- Specializes in transgender facial aesthetic surgery

- Fisher Aesthetics, North Carolina

Failure. It was mostly failure.

To start, I never—not once—got the Presidential Physical Fitness award, and not just because I couldn't qualify in the mile run, but for failing in almost every other category as well. I wasn't a popular teenager, except in those ways your parents don't want you to be popular as a teenager. I was a ballet dancer, but not an excellent one, I had wide hips and large, cumbersome breasts. I felt like an outcast. I smoked cigarettes. (Well, in that way at least, I was like most of the best ballet dancers.)

In college, I didn't complete my intended double major. I took the MCAT twice. I took the LSAT with worse results. I needed antidepressants, but concomitantly self-medicated with alcohol. I cheated on my longtime boyfriend. I was waitlisted at medical schools and never followed up because I was embarrassed I didn't get in right away. I took a job in New York in health insurance marketing in 1999, at which I was at best a mediocre employee. That failure was a particularly poor choice since it required a one-hour commute and wasn't in either a profession or an industry in which I had any interest whatsoever.

I spent beyond my means and defaulted on my credit cards. I enrolled in a PhD program that I quit a year later because I didn't want to work that hard. I was rejected from all the dental schools to which I had applied. All of them.

So yes, it often felt like one long, slow drive through "Failureland," where I was destined to repeat the same mistakes and contribute zero to the world, to my family, or to my own well-being.

It took *years* to understand that it was those very failures—some just bad luck, but most self-inflicted—that guided my progression to becoming an oral and maxillofacial surgeon.

The crazy thing is, from the outside looking in, someone tallying up my successes and good fortune would say the odds were totally stacked in my favor. They would say I had seemed driven and guided from an early age to a professional calling as a surgeon. But I just wasn't. OMFS wasn't even on my radar. No end point was on my radar. My successes weren't obvious to me, and failures seemed to overshadow everything else.

When I finally put aside my pride and begged my way into dental school, within the first week I was convinced I had made a *huge* mistake. I knew right away general dentistry wasn't for me, and I needed an escape route. I took every exam very seriously because I needed to get into a specialty. I had gone into dental school thinking what I wanted was a laid-back career with Wednesday and Friday afternoons off (heck, maybe the whole day off on Friday!), but the more I pushed myself to excel academically and clinically, the more obvious it became to me that I enjoyed working—and working hard—as long as the subject matter was interesting. I developed the "bug" for surgery.

Let me tell you about surgery. It's intense, it's exciting, and it requires precision and skill and knowledge. It made me feel like I was doing something purposeful and useful. When I was operating, I found I valued myself and my knowledge. When I completed a successful surgery, I felt that success in my bones. Chasing that feeling is part of what has driven me to the position I now have. Surgery is special to me because it is the marriage of the highly technical and the deeply thoughtful. It is the physicality of action, together with the cerebral work necessary for good judgment, that make the profession so rewarding.

And yet, if everything had "worked out" the way it was "supposed to" during high school and college, I'm confident I would be in a much different situation now. I have no idea what I'd be doing, but I'm willing to bet it would be a hell of a lot less rewarding than surgery.

I stumbled into OMFS not because I had the notion it would be the best career for me, but instead through a combination of luck (disguised as failure) and hard work. It was a miraculous fortune that I found myself in such a rewarding and arguably elite position. That's not just this professional's opinion; ask any practicing oral and maxillofacial surgeon and they'll sing the praises of a career, lifestyle, and intellectual and technical challenge that meets every target. It's simply exhilarating to obtain two doctoral degrees and the novel expertise that comes along with deep experience in two disciplines.

I am grateful for the combination of skillful technique and judgment offered by my career. Very few professions require their members to simultaneously demonstrate thoughtful judgment and precision of action. The enjoyment of purposefully and ethically deploying that unique, combined expertise is what calls surgeons back to the OR again and again, in much the same way that, for example, craftsmen who are fascinated with rebuilding old cars return to the shop day after day to progress with their work. You might say it's "Zen and the Art of Motorcycle Maintenance," but with real lives in the balance.

Although it's a fairly small specialty in terms of absolute numbers, oral and maxillofacial surgery offers many avenues to pursue. It was enchanting and thrilling to be in a residency program where every possibility—from private practice to fellowships in craniofacial, trauma, or reconstructive surgery—were available to me. I ultimately chose to complete a fellowship in cosmetic surgery. I enjoyed the visible outcomes and patient satisfaction that went along with procedures like facelifts and injectable facial fillers. This new skill set inspired a new passion— transgender facial surgery— which is a discipline that combines craniofacial surgery, cosmetic surgery, and aesthetic medicine to make a lasting, positive difference in the daily lives of patients. Gender dysphoria can be debilitating for transgender patients, and can unfortunately limit relationships, job opportunities, and assimilation into communities. The gender-affirming procedures my training allows me to perform are more than just challenging and fun for me; they are life-changing for many of my patients, which is rewarding beyond measure. Developing a practice in this subspecialty of maxillofacial surgery has instilled in me a new passion for my work, and I am grateful my surgical training has afforded me this opportunity.

Is it all sunshine and rainbows? Certainly not—my days are long, and not every operation has the exact desired outcome; there are complications. But although I usually go to sleep tired, I also go to sleep happy, fulfilled, and excited for the day to come.

I may have taken a circuitous route, but I practice what I love. In hindsight, my career was only possible because I failed so many times. All that failure, and all that picking myself up and trying again, allowed me to fall forward. I still enjoy the "routine" oral and maxillofacial surgery cases like treating deep neck space infections or repairing craniomaxillofacial trauma, but I have taken my love of cosmetic surgery to new heights with a specialized clinic treating transgender patients. I have found this niche rewarding, technically challenging, artistically satisfying, and perhaps most importantly, compatible with a fulfilling family life with my husband and three young children.

In my academic role as the residency program director in oral and maxillofacial surgery at the University of North Carolina, I know my experiences have given me compassion for my patients and the residents I teach. I work hard to ensure the residents understand failures are the key to their own self-discovery, growth, and eventual success and happiness. My own experiences of feeling like an outcast have made me particularly sensitive to others who may feel similarly. I teach that there is a path for everyone toward their passion and purpose, and we have to be gentle with ourselves and with others so we can each find that passion.

My personal journey of teaching, failure, success, determination, and compassion led me to my current position. For others, there are many different options, from office-based dentoalveolar surgery to pediatric craniofacial surgery, orthognathic surgery, trauma surgery, cancer surgery, and dental implants. In fact, the scope of oral maxillofacial surgery continues to expand, and the areas for research and practice are seemingly limitless. I'm confident many others will find their space, their rewarding career, and a life balance in the specialty of oral and maxillofacial surgery.

Bio

Dr. Fisher is a board-certified cosmetic surgeon specializing in facial aesthetic surgery. She attended medical school at the University of North Carolina, where she also completed her surgical residency program. Following residency training, she completed a fellowship in full-body and facial aesthetic surgery. Dr. Fisher is a fellow of the American College of Surgeons and has lectured nationally and internationally on facial aesthetic surgery. She has a particular interest in injectable medicines for facial rejuvenation. Her extensive training in facial surgery provides the experience and knowledge necessary for aesthetic procedures.

Stacy Geisler, DDS, PhD

- First female board certified OMFS in the history of the state of Oregon

- First surgeon to perform 3D virtual surgical treatment planning and 3D printed plates for double jaw orthognathic surgery in Oregon

- Only OMFS and PhD in epidemiology in the US

I knew from a young age that I would become a healer, even though there were no physicians, dentists or surgeons in my family.

My sister, as an infant, sustained an illness that produced severe brain damage. Her struggles and determination in living her life shaped me greatly and developed in me a drive to help others. I would say my sister's life developed within me a heart of compassion for those suffering from illness.

As a girl, I loved sewing. I would make my own clothes, crochet, and embroider. Academics also came very easily to me. I was placed in gifted accelerated programs for science and mathematics in elementary, middle, and high schools.

I financed my undergraduate college education at the University of California, Davis by working as a firefighter for the California Department of Forestry. Working as a firefighter taught me the importance of teamwork and preparedness. I also completed externships in surgical disciplines as well as nursing during this period of my life.

The time I spent as a college student observing an oral and maxillofacial surgeon sealed my decision to pursue a career as a surgeon. I liked the precision that operating inside someone's mouth required. I thought surgery performed within the mouth and jaws was amazing, since there are so many small structures close together in such a small space. I also loved the idea of helping others with my hands.

Following completion of my dental education in Ohio, I pursued training in oral and maxillofacial surgery in Texas. I discovered during my residency that I enjoyed research as well as my clinical practice. So, with the support of my husband, I completed a PhD in epidemiology funded by the National Institutes of Health in North Carolina after completing my residency.

After four years of surgical training begun in 1992 and four years of advanced doctoral education completed in 2002, I was finally ready to begin my career as an oral and maxillofacial surgeon.

I moved to Oregon in 2002 after accepting an assistant professorship at Oregon Health and Science University. I was told by the Oregon Board of Dentistry at that time that I was the first female board certified oral and maxillofacial surgeon in the state's history.

I enjoyed teaching and research at the university but found the politics of academics emotionally unrewarding. I left the university in 2005 to start my private practice in Lake Oswego. At this time, I began reviewing for the *Journal of Oral and Maxillofacial Surgery*. I also became an evidence-based reviewer for the American Dental Association and published several reviews for this journal during the early years of my private practice.

Being Oregon's first woman oral and maxillofacial surgeon has made me a type of pioneer for the state. In my private practice, I performed the first guided surgery for dental implants in 2007 and in 2018 performed the first double jaw orthognathic surgery using 3D printed titanium plates, acrylic occlusal guides, and titanium cutting jigs. I love using my scientific training to help guide me in the use of new technologies for my patients. I remain the only woman oral and maxillofacial surgeon on staff at my hospital which serves patients in Oregon, Washington, and Idaho.

During my time in private practice, I have had the privilege of mentoring several young women and men who have gone on to pursue surgical careers. These young people have become dentists, surgical ophthalmologists, and neurosurgeons. So far, no one has become an oral and maxillofacial surgeon, but my career is not yet over and I am not giving up hope!

If you asked me today what my favorite thing to do is, I would have to answer: "Operate!"

Maybe that sounds strange to you, but I truly love what I do. I feel incredibly blessed to get to remove disease that causes pain and suffering and puts things right for my patients. It is deeply satisfying to help people heal.

I love taking something that is broken and making it beautiful with my hands. This love of creating wholeness out of brokenness sustains me in my daily practice as an oral and maxillofacial surgeon.

I have a profound sense of gratitude for the patients I operate on each day. The trust and support of the physicians, dentists, and families who refer their patients and bring their loved ones to me for care gives me courage. Each patient, family member, and referral relationship is precious and not to be taken for granted.

And my heart of compassion, which was shaped so long ago by my sister and her disability, is what nourishes and drives me to be the best I can be technically and emotionally for my patients, their families, and the referring doctors I serve.

Bio

Dr. Geisler earned her undergraduate degree from the University of California, Davis, preparing her for advanced degrees in her field from Case Western Reserve University and the University of North Carolina at Chapel Hill. She graduated with honors from these programs. She completed a National Institute of Health post-doctoral fellowship at the University of North Carolina at Chapel Hill following her residency in oral and maxillofacial surgery at the University of Texas Health Science Center at Houston.

An active member of professional societies such as the American Dental Association and the American Association of Oral and Maxillofacial Surgeons, Dr. Geisler additionally supports and trains the next generation of medical professionals. She served as an assistant professor of oral and maxillofacial surgery at the Oregon Health and Sciences University from 2002 to 2005, has been an investigator on several research projects focused on clinical care and studied various aspects of head and neck cancers. These findings were published in publications including the American Journal of Epidemiology. She has served as an editorial peer reviewer for publications including Journal of the American Dental Association *and* Journal of Oral and Maxillofacial Surgery. *The latter work earned her certificates of excellence for her contributions between 2012 and 2015.*

Dr. Geisler began her early professional life as a firefighter and thus enjoys physical training such as running, weightlifting, and yoga during off hours.

A lifelong lover of the arts, she and her husband, Bill, support the Portland Center Stage Theater and Portland Museum of Art. She also enjoys spending time with Bill and their many friends.

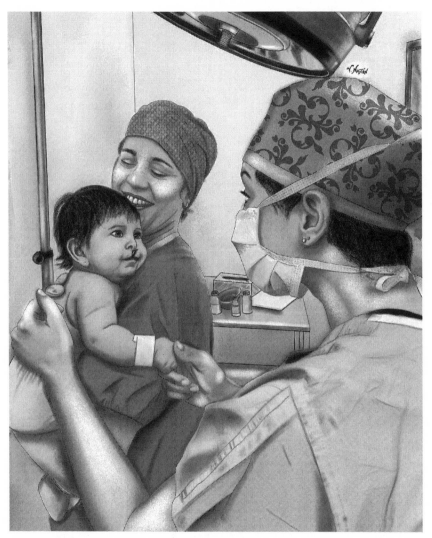

Dr. Rania A. Habib greeting a cleft baby.

Rania A. Habib, MD, DDS

- Pediatric cleft and craniofacial surgeon

- Faculty, Department of OMFS, University of Pennsylvania

- Instagram sensation with over 10K followers

- Master-level SCUBA diver and avid athlete

Ever since I was a child, I was fascinated by surgery. I was the kid to grab the first aid kit and bandage up any of my family or friends who were hurt. In high school, I was obsessed with the hit drama series, *ER*. Thursday nights I was glued to the TV, often in a trance where no one could deter my attention from the screen. I was fascinated by the intricacies of acute care and surgery.

I started my undergraduate studies as an American Heart Association scholar, where I spent the summer before freshman year in a research lab for heart devices. At the time, I decided I wanted to be a pediatric cardiothoracic surgeon. As I continued to work in the lab, the surgical residents I encountered discouraged me from pursuing a career in surgery. Approximately 80% of them told me they regretted their decision to pursue a surgical career due to the demanding hours and lifestyle required. I began to shadow different specialties in medicine and that is where I discovered the field of dentistry. To me, it was a beautiful blend of artistry, surgery, engineering, and long-term patient care. Also, in direct contrast to the surgeons I had met, 99% of the dentists I shadowed said they were happy in their profession.

I started dental school thinking I would become a general dentist, finish in four years and find my ideal job in a busy private practice. Early in my second year, I attended a riveting lecture on cleft and craniofacial surgery given by Dr. Swift, the department chairman of the OMFS Department at the University of Minnesota School of Dentistry that sparked my interest. Later that year, Dr. Ma'Ann Sabino, a fierce female oral surgeon, gave us our anesthesia lecture. I was mesmerized by her knowledge, demeanor, and surgical skill. I was equally interested in both orthodontics and pediatric dentistry, but my fascination with surgery kept drawing me back to OMFS.

At the urging of my dental school counselor, I began to shadow in the OMFS department. I made friends with the residents and attended as many department rounds and conferences my schedule would allow. I quickly realized nothing in medicine or dentistry gave me a greater rush than being in the operating room and OMFS was the perfect hybrid between surgery, medicine, and dentistry. Late in my second year, I made the decision to pursue a career in oral and maxillofacial surgery. Dr. Sabino and another OMFS faculty, Dr. David Basi, took me under their wings and spared time to answer all my questions. They shared the ins and outs of externships and practiced interview questions with me. I scheduled four externships—Mayo, Oregon Health Sciences University, Ohio State University, and University of Maryland—to ensure my exposure to the full surgical scope of OMFS.

I matched into my first choice for OMFS, the six-year program at University of Maryland, where I continued to further my medical education and honed my surgical skills in many sub-specialties of the field. It was a rough, tedious road. Even though Maryland was one of the few "female-friendly" programs at the time, there was still implicit and explicit bias toward women. I graduated and decided to pursue a career in private practice. I joined a large group practice where I mainly performed dentoalveolar surgery, implantology, anesthesia, and benign oral pathology. I quickly realized my passion was treating pediatric patients and decided to leave my lucrative job to pursue Pediatric Craniofacial Surgery Fellowship. I matched into an off-cycle position at University of Florida, Jacksonville. Upon graduation, I decided to stay in academic medicine. It is this setting that allows me to practice broader scope surgical OMFS while teaching at the dental student and resident level. My goal is to provide top-notch surgical care and improve surgical outcomes to all patients afflicted with craniofacial disorders, congenital or acquired.

Being a woman in any surgical field is tough. It tests me every single day. Despite the fact that women now comprise nearly 50% of graduating dental classes in the US, we comprise 8% of practicing OMFSs and less than 10% of academic OMFS surgeons. The ADA estimates male dentists currently earn 38% more than female dentists in the same role in private practice. So if this much adversity exists, why should women choose a career in OMFS? I do it for the love of surgery. I walk into my job everyday with gratitude that I found my calling.

Through my years of training, I developed a unique set of surgical skills that allows me to heal my patients with my hands. As a pediatric cleft and craniofacial surgeon, I get to perform life-changing reconstruction for patients who have craniofacial deformities. Nothing is more rewarding than giving a patient back form and function while promoting continued craniofacial growth. As an OMFS trained in cleft and craniofacial surgery, I use my extensive background training in medicine, dentistry, TMJ, cleft, and craniofacial procedures to make a true difference. Through the power of education, mentorship, and advocacy, I believe we will continue to push all surgical fields toward gender equality.

How do you make it as a female OMFS in a male-dominated field? These are some vital tips I wish I knew when I was training:

- While you are in dental school, shadow in the OMFS department and private practice OMFS and do a few externships. Exploring the field in its fullest will help you decide if it's the right career path for you. You should love every aspect of surgery to commit to the career or you will not be happy.

- Work hard, stay true to yourself and let your work speak for itself. Find both an advocate and a mentor to guide you throughout your career. We all need help along the way; no one makes it alone.

- Prepare for everything! Preparation shows dedication and determination. Plus, it saves a lot of heartache during difficult questioning sessions. And as the adage says, "If you stay ready, you won't need to get ready!"

- Create a good support system of trusted friends, family, and mentors to lean on during the difficult parts of your training.

- You will make mistakes. Everyone does. When that happens, take time to understand what went wrong, what you could have done differently, and most importantly, learn the lesson. Then move on with confidence. Do not let anything stand in the way of achieving your dream.

- Invest in people/experiences that bring you joy to balance out the demands of your career.

- Make time for self-care. You can't take care of anyone else if you let your own mental, physical, and emotional health lapse. Figure out what helps you relax and feel good and then make time to do those things on a consistent basis.

- Do not be afraid of the unknown. Embrace the unknown, follow your gut, and have faith. In the end, it *will* work out if it was meant to be.

OMFS is a beautiful, rewarding profession for those who are passionate about the field. Times are changing and women will continue to pioneer in surgery. I cannot wait for the day when we are equally represented in all fields. Until that day comes, I will continue to advocate for equal representation and encourage more women to pursue a career in OMFS.

Bio

Dr. Habib attended the University of Minnesota for undergraduate and dental school, graduating with honors. She completed her medical degree, general surgery internship, and oral and maxillofacial surgery residency at the six-year program at the University of Maryland Medical Center and RA Cowley Shock Trauma Center in 2015. Upon graduation, she joined a busy OMFS private group practice in Annapolis/Crofton, Maryland where she worked for two years. Always seeking personal and professional growth, Dr. Habib decided to pursue her passion of treating pediatric patients with cleft and craniofacial disorders. She completed a full scope Pediatric Craniofacial Surgery Fellowship at University of Florida, Jacksonville with Dr. Barry Steinberg. She became the first female attending surgeon in the Department of Oral and Maxillofacial Surgery at LSU, NOLA, where she was appointed an assistant professor in 2019. Her primary focus was pediatric cleft and craniomaxillofacial surgery; she served on the Our Lady of the Lake cleft and craniofacial multidisciplinary team and played a prominent role in educating surgical residents. In 2020, she joined the University of Pennsylvania faculty, where she hopes to continue to advance the field of cleft and craniofacial surgery. She is a diplomate of the American Board of Oral and Maxillofacial Surgeons. Her main surgical interests include pediatric/adult OMFS, cleft, craniofacial, orthognathic, facial trauma, obstructive sleep apnea, benign head and neck pathology, non-surgical facial rejuvenation, and facial reconstructive surgery. She is an active volunteer with Smiles International and the Global Smile Foundation, where she provides cleft and craniofacial surgical care internationally.

In her spare time, Dr. Habib enjoys traveling, rock climbing, biking, cooking, attending live music/art events, hosting events, volunteering, reading, and spending time with her family and friends. She is a master-level SCUBA diver who is also a fitness fanatic.

Leslie Halpern, MD, DDS, PhD, MPH, FACS, FICD

- Section head, Department of Oral and Maxillofacial Surgery, University of Utah

- Co-director, Office of Women in Health, Science and Medicine (WiHMS), University of Utah

- Trailblazer and mentor

I am sitting at my computer to tell a story I never thought I would write, let alone experience—without regrets of course. There are times when I look back and am amazed by how perseverance provides success. As such, I am privileged to have been a trailblazer during this journey of my career in the "wilderness" of oral and maxillofacial surgery.

I always wanted to be a doctor. I am a baby boomer and so my role models were on TV: Drs. Kildare and Ben Casey. I was raised in a family of tradition and becoming a doctor for a female was almost insurmountable unless you married one and became the "doctor's wife." I also had two male cousins who became dentists as expected.

I stumbled through junior high school in the sciences, but in high school I did well in the sciences and math. While in college as a biology major, I became a sorority sister and fell victim to the choice of being a doctor or marrying one. I also became engaged to a man who was controlling and caused me to lose my self-esteem, which I take responsibility for. We broke up in my junior year and I barely attained a 2.75 GPA—not your typical candidate who would be a shoe-in for dental/medical school, let alone, an oral and maxillofacial surgery residency.

And so, what to do? My journey involved a "waking-up" and going through graduate school where I bloomed as a PhD candidate in neuroendocrinology. I discovered a pathway for reproductive development in fish and was the first to isolate gonadotropin-releasing hormone-containing centers in the brain and pituitary gland of the freshwater teleost, Xiphophorus sp. I published an unusual number of papers for a grad student and was offered numerous jobs at universities. I wanted, however, to have an MD degree and I thought the PhD would serve as a pass, so to speak. I had three medical school interviews in New York City and was waitlisted to all. I was also married and had two sons, so it was not easy to pick up and move to another state where my chances would be better. My sister-in-law, a DDS, suggested I go to dental school since I would be able to multitask as a mom and part-time practitioner. One day I was walking by NYU College of Dentistry, went in, and amazingly was accepted because I had a PhD and was a commodity for oral health research. I was the oldest in a class of 168 (by an average of eight years) and faced adversity from my instructors and fellow students. I took out several extra student loans to help care for my children (still paying some off, but I did put my sons through college and they have no debt). This decision did cost me my marriage, and I faced other issues in my personal life, e.g., my only sister was brutally raped and murdered before her wedding day. I had to learn to compartmentalize my emotions so I could perform as a healthcare practitioner who showed compassion regardless of the situation.

I did well in dental school due to my scientific foundation and chose oral and maxillofacial surgery as my career since I worked for an oral surgeon and found it most challenging in basic science and clinical applications. My oral surgery mentors at NYU were very supportive and nominated me for Omicron Kappa Upsilon (OKU), the national dental honor society. Many others discouraged me since I was a thirty-eight-year-old fourth-year dental student; who would accept someone that age, let alone divorced and with two children, one in treatment for a rare cancer (which he beat)? I was granted four interviews and accepted into a six-year oral and maxillofacial surgery residency program in New York City. I was also accepted at a medical school where I was originally waitlisted. In addition, I was the first woman to shatter the glass ceiling in a twenty-five-year-old well-established program of men.

I was so grateful. However, I faced adversity again. During my OMFS interview, I was never asked if I had children. During my intern year, my son had a crisis and had to be treated with chemotherapy. I asked for two days off and my program director said, "I didn't know you had children. If I knew you had children I would have never accepted you. Please have your resignation on my desk in twenty-four hours." I said, "oh really," walked out, cried of course in the resident room, and went to the CIR (Committee of Interns and Residents) of the Health and Hospitals Corporation. He never pushed the envelope after that. He left when I was in my third year and the new chief of OMFS mentored residents, including me, as one should. This allowed me to finish my training. I have to say the residents in my program were all supportive of me because they never saw a woman multi-task. I was careful, however, never to take sick leave for fear that I would look weak. I hardly took a vacation for fear that my job would be filled when I was away. I was blessed to have a mother who attended every play, as well as all the little league and soccer games my children participated in. I was indeed privileged to have completed my OMFS residency and received an MD degree.

My journey continued and I went on to do several fellowships across the US in oral and maxillofacial surgery to improve my skill set. I became board certified and chose to be an academician due to my interest in clinical research. I spent a decade in Boston at a prestigious university and continued up the ladder of promotion to an assistant professor. I was privileged to have mentors who have helped women break the glass ceiling in OMFS at this institution. I received grant funding and was successful as a clinician and researcher with well-published data in peer-reviewed journals. As time went on, I realized how much I love to mentor and teach residents/students/junior faculty and was afforded an opportunity to be a program director of a residency in OMFS in the South with a promotion to associate professor. I spent five great years training residents and accomplished a successful site visit at this academic institution; 90 percent have gone on to become board certified by ABOMS. Although I was happy, I sensed a promotion to full professor would require a change of venue. I relocated to a university in the Southwest with a promotion to full professor on the tenure track. I am currently professor, and chair of oral and maxillofacial surgery at a state university's dental school. I have broadened my horizon of mentorship by serving as a co-director of the Office of Women in Health, Medicine and Science, which has allowed me to mentor not only women and students in the dental school, but female faculty throughout the other four health campuses (School of Medicine, Nursing, Pharmacy, and College of Health).

A trailblazer has an ability to craft a path for others to follow, and yet can stumble along the way. The final leg of my journey is to develop a six-year oral and maxillofacial surgery residency on my campus before I retire. Right now it is a work in progress. With all I have accomplished, I must admit there is still a lot to learn. I finished my residency in 1996 and am pleased oral and maxillofacial surgery has come a long way with a greater number of women surgeons. Yet, considering the number of programs nationally, women comprise less than 38 percent of residents. Several recent articles state that women applicants for dual degree programs are twice as likely to suffer from unprofessional behavior during their interviews.[42] The myth of "your biological clock is ticking" still exists, since there are many female residents who either have children before or become pregnant during their training and are concerned about their opportunity for training being comparable to their male cohorts who also have families. A new enemy is the gender gap with respect to promotion and opportunities in career advancement for female

---

[42] Janice H Lee, Yisi D Ji, Harvey Kushner, Leonard B Kaban, and Zachery S Peacock. *Residency Interview Experiences in Oral and Maxillofacial Surgery Differ by Gender and Affect Residency Ranking.* JOMS 77 (2019) 2179-2195

surgeons who want to be in the university setting. Glass ceilings have been shattered by some and are impenetrable for others. A recent article by Antonia Kolokythas[43] astutely states that there is a need for female role models in OMFS academic administrative leadership who rally around gender, diversity, and inclusivity as prerequisites for success, not only within OMFS, but in all careers women want to excel in. I can look back and say I have mentored at least ten to fifteen women and fourteen men who have become successful in our specialty. I thank those who I have trained and appreciate their challenging me to be a quintessential mentor.

People say that to be a mentor requires one to craft "pearls of wisdom" and so:

- When you become an advocate for yourself, your colleagues will advocate for you.

- Although glass ceilings seem impenetrable, they can provide a clear view of the road to forge an alternative path to your success.

- Stand by the courage of your convictions because it fuels the value you bring to the specialty you represent. Remember, your contributions form part of the foundation that makes your specialty strong.

- Mentees will become mentors and so the leadership pipeline will continue to build, providing innovations that surpass what their predecessors laid out.

And so, my journey, although on its final legs, is not over. There is still fire in my furnace and many more to mentor in this wilderness of our specialty. After all, isn't seventy the new sixty and sixty the new fifty? Only baby boomers know for sure!

---

[43] Pooja Gangwani, Antonia Kolokythas. *Gender Gap in Leadership in Academic Medicine and Dentistry: What Are the Barriers? What Can Be Done To Correct It?* JOMS 77 (2019) 1536-1540

Bio

Dr. Leslie Halpern received her PhD in neuroendocrinology (City University of NY) and a DDS (NYU College of Dentistry) and completed a six-year oral maxillofacial surgery program with an MD degree from New York Medical College. She has done several fellowships in basic and applied research and obtained an MPH from the Harvard School of Public Health. Dr Halpern is a diplomate of the American Board of Oral and Maxillofacial Surgery and is a fellow of the American College of Surgeons and the International College of Dentists. She has received several grants from the RWJF Center of Health Policy and the Harvard University Center of Excellence in Women's Health that focus on the identification of victims of intimate partner violence (IPV) using salivary biomarkers as risk predictors in the prognosis of health disparities in female victims exposed to violence and abuse. She currently serves as professor and section head of oral and maxillofacial surgery at the University of Utah School of Dentistry and is co-director of the Office of Women in Health, Science and Medicine (WiHMS) at the University of Utah medical campus. Her mentoring of students and dental residents and program directorship experience qualify Dr. Halpern as an essential resource for women faculty in OMFS.

I WILL NEVER QUIT

Editor's Note: *This illustration was adapted from a New York newspaper advertisement. During the first month of my residency, my chief resident jokingly posted it to the corkboard in the residents' room as a reminder not to quit. It stayed on during the entire four years of my residency. I took the clipping down when I graduated and have kept it with me to this day.*

Cathy Hung, DDS, CLC

- Founder, Morning Glory Women Dentists Network of New Jersey

- Pulling Wisdom Coaching and Workshops LLC, certified professional life coach

- Private practice, New Jersey

Uprooted and replanted.

These three words described my whole life story. Born and raised in Taipei, Taiwan, I was a happy-go-lucky child and enjoyed school during my earlier formative school years, excelling in all subjects. The biggest moment of glory in my earlier years was when I passed the rigorous mandatory high school entrance exam to enter Taipei Municipal Girl's Senior High School, the most prestigious girls' high school in Taiwan. At that time, it was such an honor that it was said to be "firework-worthy"—a celebrated event. Just a few months into the first semester in senior high (equivalent to tenth grade in the US), my father decided to migrate to Singapore and set up a factory in Malaysia. Taiwan's economy was booming in the mid-eighties and many businessmen moved to Southeast Asia for more opportunities. My parents thought it was a good idea for me to attend a local school in Singapore, where I entered mid-semester into an all-English curriculum from an all-Chinese curriculum at age of sixteen, with no preparation of any kind. The first midterm I failed English miserably as expected and resided at the bottom of the class despite decent grades from other subjects. My award-winning, prolific Chinese writing skills served no purpose and were quickly abandoned. My early glory was stripped and I had to start everything from zero. I vividly remember that the first time I opened the chemistry textbook, I spent two hours on pages one and two, checking every single word. I was able to manage to do well in math and science once I learned the key words. However, English and geography were difficult, as most of the tests were open-ended and required answers written in paragraphs. To study for geography tests, I was mumbling sentences from the textbook over and over again until I almost memorized the entire thing. I managed to memorize Malay names of towns and people, the fishing, mining, and timber industries of East and West Malaysia. I ended up graduating at the top of my class in secondary school, or O-Level, and decided to come by myself to the US in 1991 on a F-1 student visa, skipping the A-Level, as my father thought it would be a waste of time.

America was always part of the plan. Singapore was an unexpected sharp right turn, like an intermediate stop on Google Map Search. I randomly applied to California colleges using the big college handbook, did the TOEFL, and was accepted into Cal State at Fresno. I started as a double major in biology and music in piano performance and achieved Dean's List for a year. With friends' encouragement, I transferred to University of California at Berkeley during my junior year, believing I was on the path for medical school. However, I found out later that my F-1 visa restricted me from applying to medical schools everywhere. Although I was an advanced-level classical pianist, I didn't see myself embarking on a career in music. My mind was set on pursuing medical school, as I always wanted to be a doctor, but my F-1 visa status earned me several rejections from medical schools. One medical school based in California sent a rejection letter stating, "since you are not a permanent resident or a US citizen, please do not apply again." Being alone in the US, I turned to my smart friends at UCB for advice and help, and I started to look into dentistry as an attractive career choice. I was convinced this would be a profession that would allow me to pursue a career using my hand dexterity and knowledge. I shadowed at dental offices and clinics around the campus during my junior and senior years of college.

I was accepted into Columbia University and moved to the Big Apple. I had no preconceived notion of what or where I wanted to be. No one in my family was a dentist, physician, or surgeon to give me any direction. During the third year of dental school, there was a part of the curriculum in Columbia called area of concentration, where you picked a prospective specialty you planned to specialize as an elective. At the Area of Concentration Fair, each specialty set a table with information pamphlets and instruments. The oral surgery table was hovered over by big guys and I was intimidated. I ended up choosing pediatric dentistry as my area of concentration since there were more women. However, through further oral surgery rotations, the surgical procedures piqued my interest. I found myself spending spring breaks and summers doing externships in hospitals to gain extraction experience and observe various procedures in the operating room. I was then determined to apply for oral surgery.

Throughout the process of application to oral and maxillofacial surgery programs, Dr. Louis Mandel was especially supportive and helpful, and I was one of the many who benefited from his teaching and knowledge. He would give me a stack of CT scans; copies of his newsletter, *Salivary Gland Center;* and say, "go write an article, we'll publish this." When I told him I wanted to apply to oral surgery, he asked, "Why do you want to do oral surgery? Go start a family and have some kids!" Despite the jokes, Dr. Mandel was supportive and fatherly. Quirky in his own ways.

The big question for OMFS applicants has always been four or six years. To me, there was no such choice. The same issue with citizenship came up again and I simply knew six-year programs were out of the question because of the medical school admission requirements of a green card or citizenship. I was uneasy when challenged by other classmates about the number of interviews they received, mostly eight to ten. I only got three interviews, and I matched one. In the end, it didn't matter. There was someone in my class who had more than ten interviews but did not match anywhere. All you need is one match. I took a chance to bet on myself and matched. It was risky. Had I not matched, I would have to leave the US immediately because as my dental school concluded, my F-1 visa would be automatically nulled.

One shot was all it took to change my destiny. I was naive about what was about to unfold, my residency program. From the get-go, I got the "let's see how long she would last" vibes. There was a bet to see between my male co-resident and myself who's going to quit first. I was quickly exposed to acute facial trauma such as fractures and extensive lacerations, severe facial infections, and a busy clinic full of patients needing on-the-minute extractions. I learned to be a scut monkey. Being the only female in the longstanding history of male residents was tough. I didn't realize the magnitude of difficulty on all levels until later on. As a petite Asian female, patients often thought I was an assistant or nurse, and they asked for a male doctor. I was in a highly populated Spanish-speaking neighborhood. I was asked "Habla Espanol?" multiple times a day. I was sent to Spanish classes when I was still struggling with English. Almost every morning, I took the six train from the upper east side of Manhattan where I lived and transferred through the heart of Harlem to the four train to the South Bronx. I was "on the six," but I'm not J.Lo from the 'hood. The culture shock was immense.

Out of everything, being pimped on rounds was most difficult, especially for me; although I was doing well in school as a good test-taker, my reaction time was slower, and my public-speaking skills were not strong or developed. I was still translating languages in my head. Grand rounds, daily rounds, and journal clubs were more time-consuming for me to prepare for and comprehend. When English is not your first language, new words and sentences don't stick well. The more I kept piling new words and phrases into my memory bank, the more these words seemed to keep on falling out like running sand through a sieve. Sleep deprivation didn't help. There were many deer-in-the-headlight moments.

When things were rough, the clinical assistants told me stories about the first female surgeon who ever completed my program, Dr. Leslie Halpern, how she overcame her hardship to come out on top. They told me, "She's so smart, she has *four* degrees. If she could do it, you could do it, too!" The assistants offered their friendship to me and encouraged me not to give up. For that, I decided not to give up. I completed my training as the second female OMFS ever in my program history. A few months before graduation, I was offered an associate position to work in a busy group practice in the suburb of southern New Jersey. I packed up and moved to New Jersey, one of the few states that welcomed dentists with an H-1B visa at that time.

Private practice had always been my end goal. Being a solo practitioner was my dream and there was no doubt in my mind that I was going to have family and children. To top it off, I wanted to become board certified. Through two back-to-back pregnancies and childbirths, I was able to finally pass my board to become a board-certified oral and maxillofacial surgeon. The first time I took my oral board exam, I was two weeks postpartum with my firstborn and stranded in Newark Airport for a whole day as my flight to Chicago was cancelled due to a snowstorm. That was the last year the oral board was held in Chicago. I had cold sweat running down my back. Totally fatigued, I fell asleep with the book, *Oral and Maxillofacial Surgery Secrets,* still in my hand. Everything was a blur. Needless to say, I had to retake the oral board exam until I finally passed. During the 2009 economic depression, I opened a practice from scratch to be close to my family and stumbled through learning the business aspects of being a solo practice owner. The road wasn't easy but was fruitful. Referrals were not easy to come by. Some general dentists would literally look at me and laugh or scoff, saying, "What is a little girl like you doing here?" In 2019, I founded the Morning Glory Women Dentists Network of Dentists, as I found there were many local women solo dental practice owners.

My parents migrated to the US after my residency and moved to New Jersey to be near me. Not long after the move, my father was diagnosed with prostate cancer. He battled for twelve years and passed away in March 2017. I was due for my recertification board exam in September 2017. To the last of his days, he promised to help pick up his grandsons from daycare so I could prepare for my exam. Unfortunately, he didn't quite make it, and I had a hard time preparing for the recertification exam being heartbroken. I passed, but it was a tough summer. From pregnancy, childbirth, and initial board exams to family death and recertification exams ten years later, life never failed to come at me. My husband was worried and asked me, "Do you have to take the recertification? Do you need to be board certified?" I said, "Yes, I might not absolutely need to, but I want to."

Through the years, I was actively involved in my dad's care, translating and communicating with his doctors. I went through internal turmoil being on both sides of the fence as a family member and as a surgeon. It was tough translating CT and MRI scan results for dad as he deteriorated; how should I convey the results to him without making everyone go berserk? My heart sank each time reading more spread of metastasis to other organs while trying to keep a straight face while talking to my parents. There were a few emergency room admissions from the side effects of the trial drugs in my father's last days, which were very stressful.

When dad finally passed away, I knew I wanted to write about his story but I was not ready emotionally. Early in 2019, I woke up on a Sunday with a voice in my head telling me to write the book. It was meant to be a memoir, but *Pulling Wisdom: Filling The Gaps of Cross-Cultural Communication for Healthcare Providers* came through. I dedicated this book to my late father. In it, I described the language learning process, cultural adaptation, and strategies to enhance communication in a multicultural setting, drawing on my own experience. In the area where I practice, I help many first and second generation Chinese-speaking families through bilingual consultations. I am maybe the first oral and maxillofacial surgeon who's truly fluent and well-versed in medical terminology in Mandarin Chinese and English in the greater Princeton area. I take tremendous pride in my Chinese literacy skills.

Many patients don't understand the specialty of oral and maxillofacial surgery and are often surprised when I offer the option of office anesthesia; it's an unfamiliar concept to them as it is not a common practice in Asia. I wish to use my firsthand experience as a late first-generation immigrant doctor to bridge the gaps in communication due to language barriers and cultural differences. In the past year, I have devoted a lot of time between webinars, podcasts, and writing articles for publications about diversity and inclusion. In 2021, I decided to become a certified life coach and started Pulling Wisdom Coaching and Workshops LLC to help women and minority professionals like myself who face the same struggles to adjust, adapt, and accelerate in the professional world.

Do not fear to uproot yourself and replant into an unknown ground. Do your due diligence and take a leap of faith. Aside from being a surgeon, I must say I am most proud of being the mother of my two teenage boys. The best thing about being a surgeon mom is that my children grew up respecting women as surgeons because they witnessed how I juggled and managed work and family. They remembered how I used to help them with homework every night while cooking dinner after seeing a day of patients. In my children's eyes, I am their hero. I want to tell you that it is entirely possible to have a fulfilling career in surgery and have a family. There does not need to be a dichotomy between family and career.

Bio

Dr. Cathy Hung is a native of Taipei, Taiwan. She briefly lived in Singapore for two years before coming to the US alone on a student visa in 1991 at age eighteen. She earned a BA in psychology and a minor in music from the University of California, Berkeley and a DDS from Columbia University School of Dental and Oral Surgery (now College of Dental Medicine). She received her oral and maxillofacial surgery training at Lincoln Medical and Mental Health Center in the Bronx, New York. She is a fellow of American Association of Oral and Maxillofacial Surgeons and American College of Oral and Maxillofacial Surgeons. Currently, she owns a solo practice in Monroe Township, New Jersey. Dr. Hung is an alumna of the American Dental

Association's Institute for Diversity in Leadership Program and a guest blogger for ADA's "New Dentists Now" blog, where she was recognized as having "the most popular blog posts in 2020." She is an advocate of women's leadership in dentistry and surgery and founded the Morning Glory Women Dentists Network of New Jersey. She is a speaker, author, and certified professional life coach (CLC) who runs Pulling Wisdom Coaching and Workshops, LLC. Benco Dental's Incisal Magazine *recognized her as one of the Lucy Hobbs Project's "Women Who Inspire 2020." Her first book,* Pulling Wisdom: Filling the Gaps in Cross-Cultural Communication for Healthcare Providers, *is listed at the ADA Bookstore as a practice management tool. Dr. Hung served on New Jersey Dental Association's Social Media Task Force. Outside dentistry, she is also a selected member of* Forbes' *Women Forum and Rebecca Minkoff's Female Founder Collective.*

Growing up, Dr. Hung was trained as a classical pianist and composer and holds a Piano Performer's Certificate from Trinity College of London. She has produced two albums of piano original compositions, "Watercolors" and "Bay Sound," as an independent musician. She adores her Boston Sterling grand piano. Her favorite composers are Debussy, Chopin, and Liszt. She especially loves red rocks, so one of her favorite destinations is Sedona, Arizona.

Mary Kreitzer, DMD

- Trailblazer
- Primary practice (retired)

I was married during my dental school years and during residency. I have one child who was born in the fifth year of private practice. I am widowed and currently live alone and am enjoying traveling, friends, and my grandson.

The dental education at Harvard was fairly unique in that the class was small in size (twenty-one) and half of us were female. The time was mainly spent with the medical school in the first and a little less so in the second year. There were a few classes taken in the dental school, including radiology and oral pathology, but we were doing introductions to the patient and patient exams with the medical students at the various teaching hospitals.

My first patient at the dental school toward the end of the second year was a very scared fifty-year-old man who had a firm swelling in the left side of his neck slightly below the mandible. He said it had been there for about four years and he was worried it was cancer. I told him it wasn't likely, but we would ask the attending in oral medicine to examine the growth. The patient almost bolted, but I convinced him to stay. The attending wasn't completely sure and asked the clinical instructor in OMFS to take a look. After a preliminary exam and a panoramic x-ray, a large calcification was seen within what most probably was the submandibular gland; the oral surgeon was very happy to explain to the patient about the problem and that the best solution was surgical removal of the gland. And he asked me if I would like to see the procedure. Part of our experience at the medical school was being taught how to properly scrub in for procedures and perform procedures on live animals in various capacities as anesthesiologist, surgeon, and assistant, so I was more than happy to go to the OR to see the surgery performed. The patient did have a sialogram performed and the intraglandular stone was confirmed.

The OR experience at the Massachusetts General Hospital was fantastic. I was allowed to scrub in and the attending said, "Here, why don't you hold the retractor?—up close and personal instead of peering over the head of the resident, who must have been very unhappy at the time, but I was in my glory. I loved the procedure, the anatomy, and the teaching experience. I was sold! I knew I wanted to go into surgery. Fabricating dentures and partial dentures only convinced me even more that surgery was my end game.

I was married while in dental school and my husband was not in the medical or dental field. I did not want to go into academia so I did not feel I needed to pursue a double degree at the time, which was available at the Harvard/MGH program in a five-year residency. I wanted a three-year residency, but 1976 was the pivotal year when the residencies were changed to a four-year curriculum.

I went on quite a few interviews in my search for a residency. It was definitely eye-opening, with quite a few misogynists out there who didn't feel women could handle oral surgical residencies. When I interviewed at the Medical College of Virginia, I had a positive experience and could tell I would be accepted. (You get that certain vibe.)

In July 1976, I started my residency with two other men of varied backgrounds. I was the only one without a general residency and no prior experience. There were bets being made on how soon I would be leaving the program by the more senior residents. We were on call every third night and every third weekend, and of course I got the Fourth of July weekend. I was at the hospital from Friday early morning to late Tuesday night. The hospital was a major trauma center and we went to the OR six times that weekend. I loved it!

They didn't realize I was Harvard-trained in histories and physicals and I was stubborn.

Three months into the program, one of the other residents left, as it was very taxing on him and his family. We were now on call every other night and every other weekend for the next three months. We were exhausted but exhilarated. The years moved fairly quickly. We had a lot of experience in trauma and anesthesia, outpatient surgery, and some orthognathic surgery. We had no CT scans or MRIs at our beck and call, so a lot was done with panoramic films and plain films; I'm sure things were missed, but outcomes nevertheless were pretty good.

In my senior year, we were co-chiefs, as there were only two of us, and we often split rotations with a multi-person private practice office. There was a lot to be gleaned there. I had wanted to return to the Northeast and was looking for an associateship. I had several interviews but the problem was always discussed roundabout. The bottom line was I was a female and probably not in the field for the long run. I always wanted to ask if they were stupid or just dumb! I'd just put myself through four years of a very hard and taxing residency and you assume I'm not planning on staying the course. Always stick to your guns and never give in. I had one man say my training was great but the problem was I was a female and they didn't know what the referrers would do. Wouldn't fly in this day and age! They actually did not take an associate that year. (Several years later they hired a female.)

We looked for an area that would accept another oral surgeon and opened in a new building owned by dentists. Getting a loan from the bank was also interesting. I could not borrow on my own; my husband had to cosign in spite of the fact that the business was a sole proprietorship in my name only. Again, it wouldn't happen now that's for sure.

I started the practice and it was slow. No websites then, everything by phone and pencil and paper. But the practice started to grow with referrals and most importantly patient referrals. Dentists would call with medical questions quite often. Networking by going to lunch was an interesting dynamic then. When you went out, the man usually paid if it was a male oral surgeon who asked the dentist, but when I asked dentists out, it sometimes was a bit awkward; I managed to split the bills without too much arguing. Frankly it was tough, and I finally stopped doing it other than lunch-and-learn.

Five years into the practice I had my son at the age of thirty-six. I was considered a high-risk pregnancy, but I sailed through it and stayed working until the delivery date. I went back to work three weeks later and since I lived a mile away from the office, feeding was easy for me. You do what you need to do for your lifestyle. Do not compromise!

Oral and maxillofacial surgery has evolved tremendously since I finished residency. Fracture fixation with plates was just coming in; we no longer had to pass those wires. Also new were mini plates for osteotomy fixation, CT scans, MRIs, computers, implants with guided placement, all kinds of software, and the EMR. There is a huge learning curve for the older generation in the use of the armamentarium the new generation is adept at from the start!

I loved doing surgery; the procedures, although sometimes tasking, were fun to perform. The best thing is patient interaction. I loved the one-on-one camaraderie—the ability to explain to the patient what may happen and their honest gratitude for the most part. I loved the great outcomes. Working to change or correct not so great ones is a challenge in procedures and patient management but it is part of the practice of surgery.

I am a very demanding personality, so when I thought about taking an associate, I didn't think it would really work. I would in retrospect have liked to do it, but as my husband used to say, "You're not easy!" I did some volunteer work for the city of Springfield working on a homeless population but they had some interesting and harmless demands OMSNIC insurance would not cover. Needless to say, bureaucracy struck again. I also volunteered at a healthcare clinic once a week for oral surgery procedures and then got commandeered to teach the general practice residents under the auspices of NYU. More paperwork.

I retired in 2017, having undergone two knee replacements. I sold my practice to colleagues in a multi-person, multi-office practice and worked for them for a year and a half. I knew why I had stayed solo. The support was great, the personalities not so much.

I am happy to say I have been doing a bit of traveling that solo practice did not give me the luxury of doing because of the time commitment needed. I have been to Egypt and China, and plan on Vietnam and Thailand once all the infectious problems stabilize.

My advice to the younger generation is to be proactive if you want a surgical career. Get to know the attendings, ask if you can observe surgeries, know your anatomy and radiology, and keep asking questions.

Bio

Dr. Mary H. Kreitzer graduated from Barnard College in 1970 and earned a DMD from Harvard University School of Dental Medicine in 1976. She received her OMFS training at Medical College of Virginia in 1980. She entered into private practice as a solo practitioner in OMFS in July 1980 and continued in that capacity until August 2017, when she retired from practice. She also volunteered to treat the homeless in the city of Springfield for several years and worked a half day a week at a community health center as an OMFS until her retirement.

Janice Lee, DDS, MD, MS, FACS

- First oral and maxillofacial surgeon to hold a leadership role at the National Institute of Health (NIH) and first to create a craniofacial anomalies team at the NIH Clinical Center

- Chair, Special Committee for Women Oral & Maxillofacial Surgeons (AAOMS) for the first AAOMS Women OMS Special Interest Group session in 2017

- First woman surgeon to be awarded the AAOMS FEDA in 2002

- First woman surgeon to be awarded the AAOMS Gies Award in fifty-three years since its inception in 1966

I went to UCLA Dental School thinking I would become an orthodontist. But in the first week of orientation, I knew I had to be an oral and maxillofacial surgeon. I ate, slept, dreamt, read, and breathed OMFS. My journey to become an oral and maxillofacial surgeon was full of mentors—people who guided me, answered my questions, and encouraged me to pursue my passion. They were mostly men— Earl Freymiller, Charles Bertolami, and Harold Hargis—but I met Gail Strauss (shadowing her in her practice for one day) and Anh Le was my "big sister" in dental school. These women showed me that gender was not an issue, and admittedly, I never felt hindered. The same drive and passion carried me through my residency training at the Massachusetts General Hospital, where L. B. Kaban mentored me and pushed me to be a critically thinking surgeon. I could not get enough surgery and nothing was more satisfying than spending days and nights in the operating room. During residency, I learned to be resilient, direct, and focused, and learned about the importance of teamwork, because no one survives residency without working closely with your co-interns and residents. The camaraderie during OMFS and general surgery is like nothing you will experience at any other time in your life. It's a time to savor because you understand the role each person must play to make sure we "do no harm" to our patients. The sense of responsibility is also life-changing but terrifying.

Second to surgery, I found research to be an incredibly challenging but rewarding aspect of my journey. They say it's better to be lucky than good, and it was during my craniofacial research fellowship that I did the research that would eventually be published in the *New England Journal of Medicine*. No one thought it would happen, and yet revision after revision and finally publication brought the dream to reality. The curiosity to understand the disease process of fibrous dysplasia and McCune Albright syndrome coupled with persistence to complete a research study is something I never lost.

My first job as an assistant professor at UCSF OMFS taught me a few things: be kind to staff, work-life balance starts with me, and the importance of family. I was always a fast surgeon, but I became even faster, smoother, and more efficient when I had my son. I wanted to be home to cook dinner and spend time with him; nothing puts the fire under a surgeon than finding time to be with your family. You learn to juggle really well. It's hard to explain how it all happens but you do it, don't worry about it, and get the job done. Moms are great multi-taskers. I joke that residency actually trained me to be a mom, because in fact, it's harder than just being a surgeon. But it's the truth.

I am now the clinical director of the National Institute of Dental and Craniofacial Research (NIDCR) at the NIH. I've learned not to sweat the small stuff like I used to in the past. My role now is to amplify and mentor, and I rely on many peer mentors.

My "firsts": I'm the first oral and maxillofacial surgeon to hold a leadership role at the NIH and the first to create a craniofacial anomalies team at the NIH Clinical Center. I was the chair of the Special Committee for Women Oral and Maxillofacial Surgeons (AAOMS) and our committee initiated the first AAOMS Women OMS Special Interest Group session in 2017. I'm the first woman surgeon to be awarded the AAOMS FEDA in 2002 (with BJ Costello, Larry Cunningham, and Ramon Ruiz) and I'm the first woman surgeon to be awarded the AAOMS Gies Award in fifty-three years (since its inception in 1966). I may have been the first, but I won't be the last.

Bio

Dr. Lee received her DDS and MS in oral biology from the UCLA School of Dentistry and her MD from Harvard Medical School. She completed her residency in oral and maxillofacial surgery at Massachusetts General Hospital, following which she was a post-doctoral fellow in NIDCR. She subsequently joined the faculty at UCSF, where she rose through the ranks to become a professor of clinical oral and maxillofacial surgery and was recruited back to the NIDCR, where she is now the clinical director and chief of the Craniofacial Anomalies and Regeneration Section. She has received much recognition for her work on behalf of clinical researchers, including leadership roles in the UCSF Academic Senate and chair of the Faculty Council, a Champion of Diversity award from UCSF, and the Alan S. Rabson inaugural lecture at the NIH, and she was among the few women in the country chosen to participate in the Executive Leadership in Academic Medicine Program (ELAM). In September 2020, she was appointed as deputy director for Intramural Clinical Research to support clinical research and clinical researchers and clinicians at the NIH.

Dr. Lee brings expertise in surgery as well as outstanding translational research and will continue her pioneering studies on craniofacial developmental anomalies and bone regeneration.

Patricia Miller, DDS

- Attending, Harlem Hospital

- Chairperson, Blood Transfusion Committee

- Member of the board, Mavis & Ephraim Hawthorne Golden Crust Foundation for Youths

My family gave me the desire to be in the healthcare field. My mother was in pharmacy and my sister a nurse. My strongest influence came from my father, who was unable to complete medical school due to finances and hoped one of his children would continue to become a doctor. My decision to become an oral and maxillofacial surgeon took a detour through the pharmaceutical world but did not stop there.

My pursuit for knowledge led me to continue my education by obtaining my BS at Howard University College of Liberal Arts. After visiting friends in dental school and learning more about dentistry and the impact it had on people's lives, I decided to apply to dental school. I was also allowed to participate in a summer program in the dental school before my admission in the fall.

Growing up, I had a fear of the dentist. It was now my opportunity to learn the technique to calm and relate to patients who are as fearful as I was. In my senior year of dental school, I began to enjoy my oral surgery rotations, as they were not only challenging but transformational for patients and I decided on oral surgery after graduation; I was not accepted and did a GPR instead. The next year, I was accepted into a four-year OMFS program at one of New York's major trauma centers. I worked hard and had no problems in my residency, including having my daughter in my senior year.

My zeal for social work and community service led me to work in primary healthcare centers, working with people from various backgrounds, which helped me develop perspective and cultivate interpersonal skills.

Four years after being in the field, my thirst for academia sent me back as an attending part time to share my experience, knowledge, and dedication to dentistry and mentor residents in OMFS, GPR, and pedodontics.

Being the only female attending for twenty-eight years in the OMFS training program, I have been able to advocate for residents, especially females, and it afforded me the opportunity to mentor and encourage diversity in the residents and prospective applicants. My male colleagues also respect and appreciate my input and understand the concept of equal opportunity.

What we do in life matters, but how we do it, why we do it, and who we do it for matters more. Opening my office to high school students and dental students who are interested in the profession of dentistry or OMFS gives them an opportunity to see dentistry live. This I have done in my private practice and will continue to do as requested.

My advice to young women interested in OMFS is to start early with setting your goals, as early as high school. Get as much exposure to dentistry and secure all the requirements to stand out as an exceptional candidate.

Remember that positive feelings are indicators that you are moving in the right direction. You should always be bold and leap forward in the direction of your dreams. Fear and self-doubt have no place in life. Nothing should stop you as you pursue your goals with enthusiasm and confidence.

Bio

After graduating from high school, Patricia Miller attended pharmacy school at the College of Arts, Science and Technology and practiced pharmacy for a year in her homeland, Jamaica, West Indies, before emigrating to the US to continue her education.

She completed her BS in zoology at Howard University College of Liberal Arts, then her DDS at Howard University College of Dentistry.

Dr. Miller applied to the GP residency program at DC General Hospital, where she was able to get more experience in hospital dentistry, thus enhancing her application for oral surgery. She was accepted to the oral and maxillofacial surgical residency program at Harlem Hospital Center in New York City.

After working in several community health centers, she started her own private practice. But Dr. Miller's passion for academia sent her back to Harlem Hospital Center as an attending, teaching and mentoring OMFS and GP residents while maintaining her private practice on a part-time basis.

In addition to her clinical responsibilities, Dr. Miller has served on several hospital committees, including Pharmacy and Blood Transfusion. She is currently the chairperson of the Blood Transfusion Committee.

Her interest in political advocacy led her to represent the profession at the national level by being involved in AAOMS-OMPAC as a member lobbying on Capitol Hill in Washington D.C. for issues that impact the OMFS specialty and to safeguard the future of the profession.

In addition to her busy clinical practice, Dr. Miller has made time to be involved in several charitable organizations that are close to her heart, including raising funds to enhance research by running a marathon and half marathons for the American Heart Association and the Leukemia and Lymphoma Society. She is also one of the directors of the board of the Mavis & Ephraim Hawthorne Golden Crust Foundation, which sponsors scholarships for youths in the US and abroad.

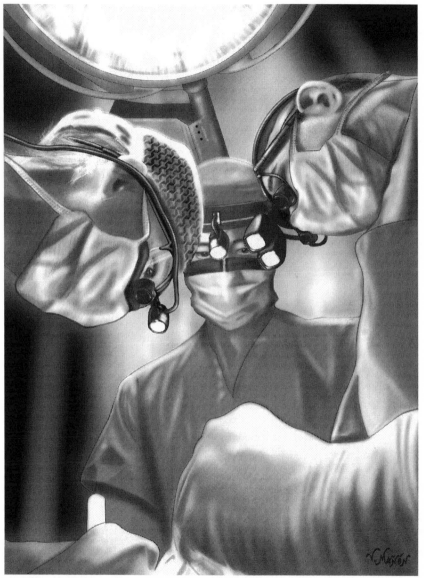

Dr. Justine Moe operating with Dr. Steven Roser.

Justine Moe, MD, DDS

- Head and neck oncologic and microvascular surgeon

- OMS Residency Program director and associate fellowship director, University of Michigan

- Lead organizer, University of Michigan Women in OMS symposium

It felt as if my journey through dentistry and oral and maxillofacial surgery residency culminated at the moment of my first microvascular anastomosis as a fellow at the University of Michigan. As I squinted through the microscope, sewing knots between 2mm vessels using a suture thinner than a human hair, I saw in the corner of my eye students, residents, and staff watching every movement intently on the microscope screen. My first solo microanastomosis. My hands trembled with excitement. The first microanastomosis of the first female OMS head and neck fellow at our institution. No pressure. I unclamped the vessels and breathed a sigh of relief as the arteries swelled up, pulsating with new life. The flap revascularized. It worked. Hours of surgery removing a large tumor of the mandible and harvesting the fibula bone for a jaw reconstruction relied on this moment—and it worked. I remember my fellowship director giving me a high five and we proceeded on to the next part of the surgery with laser-beam focus.

There are so many aspects of oral surgery that drew me to the profession, and many more that drive my continued passion for the field: the harmony of medicine and dentistry, the initial incision with a fresh blade to the skin, the dissection through complex anatomy of the neck, the satisfaction of offering transformative surgery through hidden incisions in the face.

Equally or even more impactful than the procedures themselves are the powerful relationships we develop with patients and families. As a head and neck surgeon, the relationships I cultivate with my patients are profound. I walk alongside my patients through their journey with cancer from diagnosis and treatment to surveillance, and sometimes to recurrence and death. My discussions about treatment with my patients are not only about the procedure, but also about how long after surgery it will take until they can again care for their loved ones or pets, or until they can play tennis or go skiing, or the likelihood they will make it to see their child's graduation. I have found the most meaningful moments outside of the operating room—the gratitude of a teary-eyed patient when I tell her she is cancer free, the joy of a toddler lifted into the air by a patient who I finally clear to carry his child after surgery, the goodbye of a patient who has decided to forego treatment to spend her last moments with dignity, surrounded by the love of family and friends.

I have discovered I loved many traits of surgery since I was young—the complexity of dissection, the science of health and disease, the beauty in human anatomy, and the ability to care for others; these are what ultimately drew me to a career path in oral and maxillofacial surgery. I was also fortunate to have the encouragement and support of family, friends, mentors, and coaches. My story is testament to the power of mentorship and empowerment.

I grew up in Edmonton, Alberta, Canada, as the daughter of first-generation immigrants. My parents were a constant and present influence during my upbringing. They strove to ensure that my sister and I had all we could ask for. They taught me perseverance, humility, gratitude, respect for others, and self-confidence. More than anything, they encouraged me to embrace my aspirations, and reminded me often there was no dream I could not fulfill. I have carried these values and ideals through my dental school, residency, and fellowship training, and through every day of my career to date.

I fell in love with dentistry during elementary school through my experience with orthodontics. Despite my disappointment in having to wear an unfashionable maxillary headgear for growth modification, I admired my orthodontist because he intently listened and thoughtfully responded to the curious inquiries of my ten-year-old self. In the fifth grade, for a presentation on My Future Career, I proudly told my class I was going to be a dentist, and passed around tools, brackets, and wires my orthodontist had let me borrow for the occasion.

I completed dental school at Dalhousie University in Halifax, Nova Scotia, Canada. The kind, close-knit sense of community of the Canadian Maritimes permeated the dental school and I was fortunate to have mentors who not only were passionate teachers but who also instilled a responsibility to serve the community and provide compassionate patient care. During dental school, I was drawn to the complexity of head and neck anatomy, an area of the body vital to many functions integral for survival, quality of life, self-expression, and self-identity. At Dal, I was fortunate to meet surgeons who were masters of the craft, including Dr. Archie Morrison, whose charismatic leadership transcended the operating room and the soccer field as my coach, teaching me teamwork, perseverance, and leading by example.

My OMS training at Emory University was transformative in many ways. Under the wing of Dr. Steven Roser, and through the leadership modeled by resident classes before me, I discovered the breadth of OMS, learned to deliver safe and excellent patient care, and developed meticulous surgical dissection skills. More importantly, I gained many intangible assets. I learned to self-reflect and self-assess, to think slowly, to lead gently, to embrace change, and to be an early adopter of innovation. I recall many times between OR cases spent with Dr. Roser eating graham crackers in the break room or sitting on a patient stretcher, taking time to debrief about the surgical case completed, or discuss how to optimize the flow of patient care, recent trends in the specialty or global surgery, or strategies for surgical education; the list goes on. Dr. Roser's wisdom, informed by years of thoughtful review of experiences, ongoing self-assessment, and consideration of input from all parties, is a trait I continue to admire and model.

During residency, I was increasingly drawn to the devastating disease of oral cancer, which frequently carries a poor prognosis despite appropriate treatment, and has tremendous implications for one's quality of life, appearance, and ability to interact with the world. I found mentorship in head and neck surgeons technically skilled and passionate about surgical education. Dr. Mark El-Deiry allowed me to assist for the first time in performing a microanastomosis under the microscope, patiently guiding me as I fumbled to cut sutures. Dr. Trad Wadsworth would explain the steps of a neck dissection while effortlessly carving out the anatomy of the neck using needle tip electrocautery, developing planes resembling an anatomic illustration from the pages of a Netter's textbook.

Following residency, I completed a fellowship in head and neck oncology and microvascular surgery at the University of Michigan surrounded by progressive leaders driven to continuously push the frontiers of the specialty. Drs. Brent Ward and Joseph Helman not only taught me oncologic and free-flap surgeries, including how to build a jaw from the shoulder blade and a tongue from the thigh, but also how to navigate unexpected challenges, lead with compassion, and become a progressive leader in my own right.

Now, in my third year as a practicing surgeon, my passion for OMS continues to grow. As an academic OMS, I am a surgeon, a researcher, and a teacher, among other roles. While I live and breathe surgery, I also love teaching the next generation of surgeons and engaging in meaningful research. I am inspired by the scientific pursuit of ways to optimize the detection, prevention, and treatment of oral cancer, so we can have more options to offer to our patients. Outside of work, I am a wife to an anesthesiologist and a mother to a bright and happy toddler. My husband is one of my biggest advocates and our daily schedules are a delicate dance revolving around our careers and our daughter, where flexibility, collaboration, and mutual support for each other's ambitions are key.

Throughout my training and early career, I endeavored to build my identity as an OMS first and foremost, consciously and unconsciously minimizing any part of my being that might paint me otherwise or remind others that I was in fact a woman and/or of Asian heritage. Now, I have grown to embrace these intersecting parts of my identity, and I believe this makes me a better surgeon. Just as we recognize the privilege of being a part of a patient's life and just as we, as compassionate physicians, have the moral duty to come to know the individual behind the disease, I believe it is equally as important to allow my patients to know me, the person behind the surgical mask and gown. My patients share in my personal experiences, many having showered me with baby gifts when I was expecting, and calculating the time they have been cancer-free in relation to my daughter's birthday.

This doesn't mean, however, that I have been immune to implicit bias, microaggressions, and overt discrimination in the workplace. While these experiences have led me to periods of introspection, frustration, and moments of self-doubt, I have not allowed them to impair my ability to work as a productive surgeon and passionate surgical educator. For women and minorities entering OMS, it can be difficult and perhaps impossible to be prepared for the additional challenges and adversities we will face because of core components of our individuality.

As the lead organizer of the annual University of Michigan Women in OMS symposium, my dream is to develop an inclusive culture in OMS that inspires and empowers women to become oral and maxillofacial surgeons and support women's careers in OMS such that they thrive. This is a dream that undoubtedly will take years to achieve, but we come closer through small, incremental steps. These include developing a network of female OMS for peer support, mentorship, and empowerment; creating implicit bias and bystander training for women and men in OMS and other teams across healthcare systems; strategizing standards for family support policies for men and women in the workplace; and normalizing a respectful culture in the workplace and in training, to name a few.

I have completed hundreds of free-flap surgeries since that first microanastomosis in fellowship. While that moment was pivotal, it was certainly not the endpoint of my training, despite the sense of finality I had felt at that time. I have come to realize that one's professional journey is replete with many meaningful experiences and they are ours to embrace. While we often look ahead to or wait for the next career milestone—graduation, board certification, or promotion, for example—it is important to remember there is in fact no true endpoint, no finish line to one's professional journey. My advice to my younger self, to the women and men pursuing OMS, and to my daughter, would be to show up for each moment, enjoy the journey, and be the change; cultivate in your journey the personal qualities in yourself and the culture in your environment that represent the ideal. One of my favorite quotes is from social media: "The best surgeons are the ones who are the least surgeon-y." Forge your own path, embrace your individuality, and do great things!

Bio

Dr. Justine Moe is a clinical assistant professor in the Department of Surgery, Section of Oral and Maxillofacial Surgery. She is the director of the Oral & Maxillofacial Surgery Residency and the associate director of Head & Neck Oncologic and Microvascular Reconstructive Surgery Fellowship.

Dr. Moe graduated from Emory University School of Medicine in Atlanta, Georgia and from Dalhousie University School of Dentistry in Halifax, Nova Scotia. She completed internships at the University of California, Los Angeles and at Emory University. She obtained her residency in oral and maxillofacial surgery at Emory University and completed the fellowship in head and neck oncologic and microvascular surgery at the University of Michigan.

Dr. Moe specializes in the treatment of head and neck cancer and non-cancerous tumors. Her clinical practice focuses on the comprehensive rehabilitation for facial deformities and tumor resection surgeries including reconstructive surgery, dental implant rehabilitation, and facial cosmetic procedures.

Dr. Moe recently received a national award from AAOMS for initiating a national virtual curriculum during COVID-19 pandemic, along with Dr. Elda Fisher of University of North Carolina and Dr. Carolyn Brookes at the Medical College of Wisconsin, that reached more than eighty programs of participation to provide education on a wide array of topics and maximize resident education.

Tania Nkangula, DDS

• Private practice, Maryland

I don't remember the fear when my teeth got loose and came out. I'm sure there were family members who coached me along, but when I lost my first tooth, I felt empowered to go on and coach my little friends. This was in the rolling hills of southern Malawi, surrounded by rolling steep hills and unpaved roads. I remember poinsettias—the Christmas plants being outdoor trees we played under, and it was that memory years later brought me to question if I had been destined to become an oral and maxillofacial surgeon. As I write about myself, I know there is more to life and I'm not done yet.

I didn't think much about dentistry until I was in college and a friend of mine encouraged me to consider it. I wanted to be in healthcare and didn't know if delivering babies at all hours of the day and night would be appealing. I wanted to have a profession with "good mommy hours." I wanted to treat healthy patients, go home at the end of the day, and have time for family. Little did I know that while I thought I was running away from hard work-medicine, I would land right where I had wanted to avoid—taking care of those who are ill, and sometimes having late hours. And as my teenage daughter is applying to college, I realize if I am ever in need to occupy my time, there remain many options and opportunities.

I was lucky to get accepted to Howard University College of Dentistry right out of college. Before school had started, I had the opportunity to shadow a dentist in the small town of College Place, Washington, where I went to school. The kind dentist gave me the opportunity to come as often as I wished. On the first day,

I remember sitting near the chair; the patients would come and greet him warmly, take out their dentures, and have conversations I couldn't understand. I failed to get excited about my new chosen profession, but I also didn't develop a fear. Around the same time, I read an article in a magazine about an oral surgeon, Dr. Renee McCoy-Collins. I was even more excited when at the end of my first year in dental school she talked to our class.

For the first time in my life, I saw someone who gave me inspiration and hope that maybe I, too, could follow her lead. Going back to college, Dr. Perrin, my college final college advisor, was assigned the task to ensure I graduated on time. He was working with an academic butterfly— that student who changes majors because they aren't sure what they want to follow. I switched from biology to health sciences after my parents informed me I couldn't go into pre-law or any other majors. When I informed Dr. Perrin that I wanted to go to dental school, he asked me, "Are you sure you will get in?" He recommended I pursue hospital administration. I am glad that I listened to the voice within that didn't agree. He was my advisor—the one who would teach me how to unlock my dreams only to discover that sometimes, many times, we have to take the bad suggestions and confirm the negatives. Hospital administration was not for me and I have never looked back.

I am so grateful there are more women in oral and maxillofacial surgery who have befriended me. I am grateful that from inside, the road isn't always easy, but we are not alone. I am so grateful for the friends I made in residency. I was the first woman at Meharry Medical College, and upon the completion of my program, Dr. Bennett informed me I had left my mark on it. I was able to find a way to let him know that impact works both ways. While we may endure challenges, do we see the opportunity within to speak the ideal? In my third year of residency, the second year resident, the second woman accepted into the program, observed that Dr. Bennett treated the first year differently than how he treated me. She felt like he was nicer to the other residents, and they got along so well. I pointed out to her that I loved operating with the intern because while the intern and Dr. Bennett talked about hunting and other such sports, I was able to do more surgery under less critical environments. What I didn't mention was that there were a few fundamental beliefs I held to keep me focused on my end goal.

- Know the rules. I was taught that there was a hierarchy—and it was my responsibility to honor the direction of the person senior to me before complaining. My adherence to the protocol was brought into question when the resident ahead of me reported that I had a bad attitude toward his direction. I was called to my first meeting with the program director. When I was presented with the problem, and I explained the facts—I didn't dislike how the resident spoke to me but had concern about his medical facts, or lack thereof—I was no longer "in trouble." Thus, while honoring the hierarchy, attitude and aptitude go hand in hand: have a good command on facts.

- Create a personal priority list. I had never been called names in my professional life and was so embarrassed in surgery when in my first year I was called a "hard-headed heifer." It was my first year, new to the VA hospital where there was no safety in fellow residents. We were taking out teeth, and perhaps I didn't hold the retractor or suction correctly, and I was name-called. I told myself, no crying. As I fought back the internal tears, it was everything I could do to finish the case without letting it show how much those words stung. In the quiet of my apartment, I made a list of who mattered most and where they fit. At that time, the surgeon I was working with was new to my life, and so even though I really wanted to make a big impression, he had not invested in me as had other family members along the way, so he fell toward the lower part of my priority list. This meant that while the disparaging name-calling could be cast aside, the praise and good he gave also had to be tempered to where he stood on the list. I also knew I had to address this name-calling to the person, and a few months later, at an unrelated event, I was able to bring it up and own the moment. Sometimes, we have to get to the point of injury and really let go of the pain and find the absurdity in the situation, letting it go or staying forever wounded.

- Create a timeline. Early on, I wanted to quit the program. Things weren't going well, and I was unhappy. I gave myself permission to quit. I also set in place a condition for exiting the program. I had to go out with a bang. I didn't know where I would find that critical moment, but upon my departure, I would want to leave for a significant cause. Well, the day would start with me looking for the moment of exit, and the days would end with no compelling reason to quit. Toward the ending of my second year, I decided I had now reached the halfway mark and wanted the certificate of completion. So I put the balance of my life into the program. Each time I got discouraged, I would tap my watch symbolically to remember there was an end date in sight. I soon became determined to make sure I graduated with a certificate for the time spent.

It has been almost twenty years since completion of my training. I find the longer I stay in the profession, the smaller the world of dentistry and oral and maxillofacial surgery becomes. I have been blessed to see my family evolve. Motherhood is still the role that has been the most demanding and challenging. I look with wonder at my beautiful sixteen-year-old daughter as she discovers and develops her talents and skills. I crack up at how she finds humor in the strangest of times, and I am thankful for the joy she brings. And as she finishes up her junior year of high school, I ask myself, where did the time go? I went to many gymnastic competitions and yet feel the pang of loss at the many things I missed out on. There has to be a give and take. Oprah Winfrey has said, "You can have it all. Just not all at once." I ask myself, what is the next step?

Professionally, I am now interested in lasers in surgery, particularity with biostimulation and affecting pain, improving airways, and rejuvenation. The biggest gift that I would like to contribute to others is in the area of improving documentation. If there was a way to give back time, it would be in cutting back the hours spent with a laptop completing notes to focus on living in the moment.

Bio

Dr. Nkungula is originally from Malawi. She earned a BS at Walla Walla University, Washington and DDS from Howard University, and took a year of GPR at Columbia University before her oral and maxillofacial surgery training at Meharry Medical College of Tennessee. She is a diplomate of American Board of Oral and Maxillofacial Surgeons and is currently practicing in private practice in Maryland. She is a member of several professional associations, including ADA, AAOMS, AAWD, Maryland State Dental Association, and Maryland Society of Oral and Maxillofacial Surgeons.

Dr. Riddhi Patel and Dr. Maryam Akbari

OralMaxFax podcast, the first podcast in oral and maxillofacial surgery hosted by two female surgeons

About OralMaxFax

Dr. Maryam Akbari is an OMS resident in New York City. Dr. Riddhi Patel is a board-certified oral and maxillofacial surgeon practicing in Cleveland, Ohio. OralMaxFax is the first podcast in oral and maxillofacial surgery hosted by two female surgeons who are also friends. They discuss the diagnosis and treatment of oral and maxillofacial diseases, injuries, and defects in an engaging podcast dialogue. Some of the episodes can also be found on ACOMS.org.

Instagram@OralMaxFax

Riddhi Patel, DMD

- Oral and maxillofacial surgeon; Cleveland, Ohio

- Co-founder, OralMaxFax podcast

In May 2014, when I was crossing a street in Baltimore, I received a phone call from Dr. Vincent Carrao, a call that changed the trajectory of my life. He said, "Hi Riddhi. We would like to offer you a position for residency at Mount Sinai Hospital." At first, I was speechless. Dr. Carrao was probably thinking maybe I changed my mind—hello? Ha! But in all honesty, I just couldn't believe that everything I had dreamed of and hoped for was finally going to come true. Needless to say I said yes after safely crossing the street. So the first thing I would like to do is to take a moment to thank all my mentors who invested in me and believed in me.

I take great pleasure in writing this personal story for the American Dental Association's women in the oral and maxillofacial surgery book project. More than ten years ago, I started this journey in dentistry at the University of Pennsylvania, not exactly knowing where I wanted to go after or what I wanted to do next in my life. All I knew was that I had accomplished a big milestone in my life by choosing a career that would allow me to be creative with my hands and help restore smiles on people's faces. Dental school was undoubtedly a lot of hard work, but those were the most cherished days of my life, where I met some of the best people I will ever know. As I was approaching the end of my third year in dental school, I knew I had to make a decision and choose my path onward. The turning point in my life was the anatomy lab with cadaveric dissection. I thoroughly enjoyed being in that class, learning anatomy and dissection. But it wasn't until later on as an anatomy teaching assistant when I realized my love for dissection and teaching anatomy. This is when I knew my choice was clear. I solidified my decision to become an oral and maxillofacial surgeon.

However, this decision did not come without challenges. One thing I learned early on in my life is to always believe in myself. But was that enough to get me to where I wanted to be ten years after making that decision? As I researched the specialty and learned more about the residency process, I quickly realized it had a false impression of being a specialty for men. I distinctly remember one of my male friends, who was also applying to be an OMS, telling me I had more of an orthodontics type personality and I should reconsider my decision to be a surgeon. Even more surprising was that most women in dentistry truly believed that becoming an OMS would hinder their life goal of having a family and deprive them of the flexibility to spend time with family. Well, I wasn't going to take someone's word for it; I wanted to see for myself. Life's biggest lessons are not learned if you don't challenge yourself and allow yourself to take the path less traveled. And here I am now ten years later writing this personal story about my journey to OMS.

Residency at Mount Sinai Hospital in New York was no walk in the (Central) park. There were many long hours and sleepless nights, but I truly enjoyed my residency program. I found some of the great mentors and friends in life. I was fortunate enough to train under some of the best surgeons, who also cared deeply about my education. There were times when it was frustrating and we all went through phases of "why am I doing this," but there were far more instances that confirmed my decision to become an oral surgeon. I was given a real opportunity to make positive changes in my patients' lives and it's the smile on their faces that makes this career most rewarding. We traveled through four hospitals in different boroughs of New York City to gain exposure to all different aspects of OMS, from facial trauma, pathology, orthognathic surgery, and temporomandibular joint surgeries to dental implants. Building a strong foundation requires guidance from effective, strong leaders and I was lucky to work alongside more than ten different faculty members who all taught me tips and tricks that helped me better my surgical skills and thinking process for any given case. It was always a dream of mine to learn more about cleft lip and palate surgeries. This dream finally came true during my chief year in residency, when I had the distinct opportunity to travel to Bolivia through the Healing the Children Northeast chapter with my mentor. What I took away from that experience was far more than just surgical skills. During my short week in Bolivia working alongside other specialties, including pediatrics, anesthesia, nursing, and speech therapists, every one of them donating their time for a greater cause, I learned how important it is to be selfless, giving, and working toward a greater good. It's these humbling qualities that sets a great surgeon apart from a good surgeon.

The end of my residency was certainly not the end of my learning, nor should it be. It is, rather, only the beginning. One thing I want to drive home today is that we are all lifelong learners and we must always evolve with time and take opportunities or even create opportunities to make new dreams and new goals. It's this desire to continue to learn and help others learn that led to the inception of my podcast OralMaxFax, the first podcast ever in OMS. My friend, Maryam Akbari (who is also a female resident at Mount Sinai Hospital) and I realized we were lacking effective ways of learning in our field. We took matters in our own hands and decided to make a podcast to help with our education as well as help others learn more effectively. If we are to keep up with our medical colleagues we need to start somewhere, and that's when OralMaxFax was conceived. Our main goal with this podcast is to bring evidence-based learning for our listeners. Most residents realize that once you are at this stage of your education you don't necessarily learn everything from books. There are a lot of gray areas at this point in learning and we had to look at many resources to find answers. OralMaxFax strives to put together a comprehensive review in an easy to learn format. And we all know podcasts are so easy to listen to while doing everyday activities such as driving, cooking, jogging, biking, or even riding on a train. I encourage all of you to continue to learn new things, advance in life in multiple domains, find mentors to guide you, and have fun along the way.

Always be humble and try to be a better version of yourself each and every day. If you are reading this, you are already halfway there; don't let ifs, ands, or buts in your life prevent you from achieving your dreams. I want to emphasize that young women need to know their career and family lives are not opposed. Find your own definition of success and break free from the limitations placed on you by society. My career choices did not get in the way of my life. I want to share that I chose to get married while in residency to an extremely supporting and loving partner, and now we are welcoming our first baby girl this year. I am proud to say that I am a successful female, American board-certified oral and maxillofacial surgeon—and you can be, too!

Bio

Dr. Riddhi Patel is a practicing oral and maxillofacial surgeon in Cleveland, Ohio. She earned a BS in biology from Furman University and a DMD from the University of Pennsylvania, Philadelphia. She received her oral and maxillofacial surgery training at Mount Sinai Hospital in New York. She is a diplomate of American Board of Oral and Maxillofacial Surgeons, American Association of Oral and Maxillofacial Surgeons, and American College of Oral and Maxillofacial Surgeons. Dr. Patel has held many diverse positions in her career, including clinical instructor at University of Cincinnati, clinical assistant professor at Case Western Reserve University and attending surgeon at Metrohealth Hospital in Cleveland. Currently, she is a practicing surgeon at the ClearChoice Dental Implant Center in Cleveland. Dr. Patel has had many publications in the field of OMS and some of her interests include implant dentistry, facial trauma, pathology, and reconstruction. She is one of the founding members of the first evidence-based oral and maxillofacial surgery podcast, OralMaxFax. Dr. Patel is fond of traveling, diverse cuisines, cooking, and art.

Resident Special Feature: Maryam Akbari, DMD, MPH, MD

Dr. Maryam Akbari is an Iranian-American oral and maxillofacial surgery resident at Mount Sinai health system. Along with Dr. Patel, she co-founded OralMaxFax, the medical community's first oral and maxillofacial podcast.

As a teenager, she immigrated to Bloomington, Indiana, after finishing high school in Iran. After completing her undergraduate degree from Indiana University, Dr. Akbari started a dual degree program—DMD and MPH—at the University of Pennsylvania. As she finished her programs, she found oral and maxillofacial surgery to be the perfect bridge between dentistry and medicine to have the most impact on her patients and the wider community.

The OralMaxFax podcast manifested as a result of several nights out where Drs. Patel and Akbari talked about ways to enhance accessibility of evidence-based resident learning. An innovative educator, Dr. Akbari believes enhanced patient care in OMS depends on rigorous educational groundwork, setting a foundation for practitioner growth and the continual pursuit of gaps in our knowledge. For her, the feasibility of access to evidence-based information is the first step in laying that groundwork.

In addition to OralMaxFax, Dr. Akbari is on the editorial board for the "Residents' Corner" for *The Journal of Oral and Maxillofacial Surgery,* the women's committee of ResidentsROAAOMS, and the surgical committee of Mount Sinai health system. Dr. Akbari willl join the Lincoln Medical and Mental Health Center as faculty after graduation.

Elisheva Rosenfeld, DDS, MD, FACS

- Northwell Cleft Palate and Craniofacial Center

- Northwell Sleep Center

- Northshore University Center

- The New York Center for Orthognathic and Maxillofacial Surgery

The story of how I found my career starts with my mother and her career. I am the daughter of an OBGYN mother. And not just any OBGYN. My mom is a solo practitioner and delivers over 650 babies annually. That's 1.78 babies delivered per day. As far back as I can remember, she was always extremely busy, never sitting in one spot for more than a few seconds. She survived on coffee and catnaps that punctuated her otherwise whirling dervish lifestyle. Her pager went off at the absolute worst times, mostly right before I was about to pour out my heart to her about some adolescent existential crisis. At my own wedding, she left for the hospital before the end of the reception to deliver twins. But this was by no means absurd; on the contrary, this was normal for me.

Growing up, naturally I harbored a lot of resentment for that dreaded pager, but eventually I grew accustomed to it, and later in life I learned to appreciate it. I could see that my mother truly loved her job, loved bringing babies into this world. I saw how much her patients appreciated her hard and tireless work, with all the flowers, gifts, and cards she brought home from the office. Everywhere we went when I was growing up, we would run into her patients or her patients' families, and they would clamor to talk to her as if she was a celebrity. I also appreciated how she always came to the rescue when I or one of my siblings was sick, and she always knew exactly what to do. I could see that her passion for her work carried her through all her stress and sleep deprivation. She had these magical medical superpowers, and I was intrigued. I wanted to find that passion in something myself.

So naturally, I thought I would just follow in her footsteps and become an OBGYN. That aspiration lasted until college, when life got real, I got married, and I just didn't want to have her crazy lifestyle. The epiphany hit me pretty suddenly when it came time to think about applications to medical school. I realized I lacked her unwavering drive to wake up in the middle of the night and leave my warm cozy bed to deliver a baby. She had dreamed of delivering babies since she was six years old. I most certainly had not. I didn't know what I wanted, but I knew I wanted to take care of patients in some capacity. I wanted to understand the body and its workings better so I could help people, as I had seen my mother do for so many people. But most of all, I wanted to feel passion for what I did, because I knew it was passion that was the driving force to excel.

This great epiphany gave way to a bit of a crisis when I found myself nearing the end of my sophomore year of college, unsure of my future path. It was actually my mother who suggested, and then encouraged, my application to dental school. She thought it would satisfy my desire to take care of patients but would provide a more forgiving lifestyle than a career in medicine. We did not have any dentists in the family, on either side, and I knew nothing about the field. But I had to move toward some career path, and so I applied and was accepted. It was a strange feeling pursuing this new field, having thought for most of my young life that I would follow in my mother's footsteps.

I enjoyed the first couple of years of dental school. It was a whole new world that I had absolutely no background in, no preconceived notions, and unlike many of my classmates, no plans or ideas of the different specialties that existed. I was truly a blank canvas, and thoroughly immersed myself in each class, really trying to absorb and internalize the information, waiting for something to spark my interest. It was fun working with the different materials, sculpting teeth out of wax, making dentures and crowns. At first, I seriously thought I would pursue a career in general dentistry, because I enjoyed everything and I didn't gravitate toward any specialty in particular. But after some time, general dentistry felt lacking to me; I didn't feel the same excitement about it that I had when it was all new. And that was acceptable to me, because by that time, I had had my first child and was pregnant with my second and being a general dentist would afford me the career flexibility that would be conducive to raising my children. So the convenience of a career in general dentistry, plus a lack of passion for any particular field, was really what propelled me in that direction.

Then came my third year of dental school, and I was exposed to the oral and maxillofacial surgery specialty for the first time. It sounds completely silly to say, but it was like meeting my soulmate. I just felt something I couldn't describe, like a deep connection, drawing me in. I loved the vast scope of the specialty: extracting teeth, bone grafting, dental implants, repairing cleft palates, corrective jaw surgery for skeletal deformities, management of TMJ disorders, sleep apnea, facial trauma, and jaw pathology and cancer. I absolutely loved that the field involved and required knowledge of medicine, and even incorporated a medical school education into one of the residency tracks. I was inspired. I was in love!

I promptly began doing all I could to find out more. My dental school did not have a very strong oral surgery presence for the students, so I had to go seek out the information and experience myself. I researched the different residency programs. I applied for externships at the programs at the top of my list. I spent as much time as I could in the oral surgery clinic, shadowing the residents, helping them out with seeing patients, and extracting as much information as I could from them about the culture of the OMFS residency program. And I confirmed for myself that this was the field I was meant to pursue. I never looked at the clock, because the time would pass very quickly when I was in the OMFS clinic or in the OR. Across the board, residents and attendings alike would glance at my second trimester belly and an unmistakable look of doubt shadowed their faces as they spoke to me. But no one explicitly discouraged me from pursuing the specialty. On the contrary, I found most OMFS residents and attendings were very encouraging and supportive. Interestingly, my own classmates were my biggest critics. They told me I would never make it through, or that to succeed I would have to be a terrible mother and not see my children for six years. I refused to believe this, mostly because I thought about my own mother. I thought about how passionate she was and still is about her career and realized if I truly felt a genuine passion for the field of oral surgery, which I did, I would be able to make it through the residency, and my children would appreciate this about me in years to come.

Of course, making it through the residency was easy. It was leaving my children at home with my then husband/parents/in-laws that was difficult. I had to have a meeting with all of the resources in my immediate and extended family, because it was no small request to ask of them. It truly takes a village, as the saying goes. The answer was, of course, a unanimous "yes," and I began my journey to pursue my passion. I still cannot believe how lucky I was to have the tremendous family support I had. Had I not had that support to help with raising my three children (I had my third child during the medical school part of the residency), I can say with absolute certainty I would not have been able to make it through the residency. It was grueling, both physically and emotionally, and tested my resolve to the very core of my being. But I don't think a day went by that I wasn't happy and thankful to be there.

I am now in a group oral and maxillofacial surgery practice, and I couldn't be happier. I repair complex facial injuries and correct skeletal deformities of the face. I participate in a cleft and craniofacial team and an obstructive sleep apnea team. I perform temporomandibular joint arthroscopy, open arthroplasty, and total joint replacements. I perform excisions of jaw pathology. I maintain hospital privileges and take emergency trauma calls at four local hospitals. I lecture and teach students and residents, as well as educating other departments in the hospitals. I struggle constantly to balance my career with raising my three wonderful boys. I still rely on help from my family, because now their demands are carpools, help with homework, and emotional support in dealing with middle school drama. But I am infinitely more present for them than I was when they were in diapers, and they do not feel they missed anything. They feel loved and nurtured, and I can see they are beginning to appreciate the dedication and passion I have for my career. When I step back and look at the path I chose, I smile at the irony. I applied to dental school to avoid the demanding career my mother had. And now, I have a similarly demanding job, but one I am excited about. When I get that phone call in the middle of the night for a gunshot wound to the face, I don't mind leaving my cozy bed.

Bio

Dr. Rosenfeld earned her dental degree from Stony Brook University School of Dental Medicine and her medical degree from Stony Brook University School of Medicine. She completed the six-year advanced training in oral and maxillofacial surgery at the prestigious Long Island Jewish Medical Center, where she served as chief resident from 2013– 2014. She received her board certification and currently practices the full scope of oral and maxillofacial surgery. She operates at Long Island Jewish Medical Center, New York Hospital, Cornell-Weill Medical Center, and North Shore University Hospital, and she is actively involved in resident education at all three institutions. Dr. Rosenfeld has a particular interest in orthognathic surgery, cleft and craniofacial reconstruction, and treatment of maxillofacial trauma. She serves on the Northwell Cleft Palate and Craniofacial Center, the Northwell Sleep Center, and the Advanced Facial Trauma and Reconstruction Team at North Shore University Hospital. Dr. Rosenfeld is a fellow of the American College of Surgeons, an educational association whose physicians must pass a set of rigorous qualifications for membership.

Debra Sacco, DMD, MD

- First female member, AAOMS board of trustees

- Board examiner, American Board of Oral and Maxillofacial Surgeons

- Oral and Maxillofacial Surgery Associates, North Carolina

Some doctors will identify one thing that led them to explore entering the medical profession. That was not the case for me. No TV shows with esteemed doctors, no relatives in medicine, and no notable personal health experiences, just a calling from as far back as my memory will allow. In the seventies and eighties, most women who entered healthcare were nurses or allied staff members. I had other goals. I wanted to be a doctor. Each year, I contacted the local New York hospital to check the minimum age to become a candy striper. Becoming a candy striper was the way I would gain early exposure to the science and the secret world of medicine. Eventually, I was able to take the necessary course to become a candy striper. I learned how to roll and transport patients, the proper hospital protocol, how to transport patients, and how to perform various other tasks. I meticulously paid attention to every detail. I was ready. At the end of the class, I was excited to receive my certificate, striped jumper, and white shoes that made me feel as if I was on my way to becoming a doctor.

Being a part of the hospital team felt comfortable and I enjoyed helping the patients. I was fortunate to initially be assigned to physical therapy and work side by side with burn patients, amputees, and orthopedic surgery patients. As a young teen, I did not find their wounds distressing, but rather it served to incite more curiosity about their injuries and treatment. Each time I rotated to a new area I was nervous upon my arrival, but this always transitioned into eagerness once asked to aid with patient care tasks. While I made mistakes that led to embarrassment, every day I left feeling reassured that I was meant to have a career in medicine. While I worked in many areas of the hospital, I found myself always hoping to be assigned to one of the surgical floors. The ability of a surgeon to use their hands and mind to heal was intriguing. Each day offered me bits of information that ultimately led me to the library to learn more.

One day, I entered the damp basement looking for the tall stern nurse to give my floor assignment. She instructed me to find the hospital dental clinic. I made the long walk wondering how this fit in with my long-range plans. When I arrived at the clinic, the oral and maxillofacial surgeon saw me standing at the door as I waited to find the right moment to introduce myself. He turned to me and introduced the patient and the complex surgery planned. This patient's lower jaw was positioned a centimeter in front of the upper jaw and he was going to surgically correct this. Now he had my attention. He would use a saw to create cuts in both the upper and lower jaw, reposition them in the proper anatomical position, and then wire the jaws together for six weeks as the patient healed. I had a hard time envisioning this. The next day I had the opportunity to see this patient's transformation after surgery. The surgeon showed me drawings, photographs, and textbooks about the intricacies of this surgery and explained the functional and esthetic benefits. While walking home that day, I imagined the possibility of becoming an OMS. Through conversations I learned OMS requires intellectual abilities, physical dexterity, and a strong work ethic. Our specialty is a beautiful synthesis of science and art.

If I was to become an oral and maxillofacial surgeon, I knew tuition for college, dental, and medical school would be significant. I attended the State University of New York at Binghamton for college, as it had an excellent reputation, provided challenging courses, and was held in high regard by medical and dental schools. During dental school at the University of Connecticut, I was able to complete research in cleft lip and palate under Dr. Poole, shadowed Dr. David Todd (an intern in OMS at the time), and worked under

Drs. Hupp, Shafer, and Assael. Their mentorship, enthusiasm about OMS, and encouragement solidified my decision to become an oral and maxillofacial surgeon. While a dental student, I worked as a caterer and babysitter to help pay for my tuition. I was determined to graduate without significant debt so I would have more career choices after residency.

As I applied to residency programs, the first patient I met in the dental clinic on Staten Island, New York was fixed in my mind as I realized I was about to train how to do that surgery. While a resident at the University of North Carolina in Chapel Hill, I trained under Drs. Terry, Tucker, Turvey, White, and Zuniga. I found residency rewarding and the faculty invested in my education. The faculty's enthusiasm about oral and maxillofacial surgery kept me energized throughout my training. I still remember the anticipation I had the first time Dr. Turvey handed me the saw to create the cuts in the maxilla. My time in medical school and year of general surgery provided me with further knowledge and confidence, and reinforced that OMS is the best profession of all. Oral and Maxillofacial surgery combines science, anatomy, and creativity while demanding a good interpersonal skill set and manual dexterity.

Following completion of the residency, I explored positions at several academic institutions, as I felt a calling to teach, perform surgery, and mentor students. I decided to continue as a full-time faculty at UNC following residency. Dr Bill Profitt, the orthodontist who was integral in surgical orthodontic care, would be working with me as a new attending. His camaraderie and mentorship were significant in fine-tuning my understanding of orthognathic surgery. I was also able to forge close working relationships with the prosthodontic faculty at UNC that continue to this day. It is rewarding to be able to work with other specialties in the team approach to our patients. As a young academician, I was the course director for local anesthesia and medical emergency courses for the second-year dental students. I truly enjoyed this role and felt a responsibility to the students.

Balancing family, work, and personal interests can be challenging. While on the faculty at UNC, I had our first daughter, Emma, who is now twenty-three. One day while walking to the parking deck with the pediatric dentistry residents, they questioned how I balanced everything. My quick response was, "good communication between my husband and myself." When I arrived home, I quickly realized we had both forgotten to bring Emma home from daycare. So much for good communication. We also had a second daughter, Alaina, who at eighteen is fascinated by surgery. Time management can be challenging with a young family. Over the years I have done my best to be available to them during swim meets and other important moments, but there are times when I have missed family events. It is important to have people and resources you can rely on for help. For our family, it meant my husband closed his law practice to be home with our girls. Each individual must choose their own path and not judge others, or even themselves at times.

Currently, I practice in a four-doctor practice with three locations near where I trained. This specialty has allowed me to have control over my schedule and perform surgeries I enjoy while spending time with my family. I continue to see trauma and infection patients at the local hospital, bring elective surgery patients to the surgical centers for surgical repositioning of their jaws, and have a robust office practice as well. While patients may come to see me with similar surgical issues, they have different medical and personal concerns that must be taken into account. My goal is to provide patients with information so they can make an informed decision to achieve functional and esthetic results with current technology available. Each patient should be made to feel as if you are caring for them the way you would like your family member to be cared for. If you practice in this manner, the personal rewards are significant. When we care for them as individuals and address their unique needs, we have the ability to create a lasting impact personally as well as surgically.

Since the specialty of oral and maxillofacial surgery has given me so much, it has been important for me to give back through service. I have served as a board examiner, participated as a member and chair of numerous committees on the state and national level, and served on the executive committee of our hospital. Currently, I am privileged to be able to serve our national organization, the AAOMS, as the first female trustee. I am grateful to the women who have gone before me and look forward to being able to provide my perspective to our specialty while I continue to represent us all. The profession of OMS allows us to challenge ourselves academically and provide a service to patients that impacts their lives.

Throughout my training and career, I have been privileged to have mentors and friends who have fortified my strengths and assisted me in finding solutions to challenges. There were times where gender bias and discrimination occurred, but by focusing on working hard and patient care, seeking support from peers, and treating others with kindness, I have grown from all experiences. Every individual will face challenges, but it is up to each person how they respond. To remain grounded and successful, surround yourself with others who support you, maintain interests outside OMS, find a mentor regardless of their age or gender, and most importantly be true to yourself.

Bio

Dr. Sacco graduated from the University of Connecticut School of Dental Medicine and University of North Carolina School of Medicine. Following completion of an internship in general surgery and residency in oral and maxillofacial surgery, she was a full-time faculty member at UNC.

Dr. Sacco maintains board certification and has also served as an examiner for the American Board of Oral and Maxillofacial Surgery. She has served the specialty on numerous committees for the American Association of Oral and Maxillofacial Surgery (AAOMS) and OMSNIC. *Through the Osteo Science Foundation, she serves as a member to OMS residents through their clinical observership program. Currently, she serves as trustee for District III for the AAOMS. Dr. Sacco is on the hospital staff at NC Specialty Hospital, Duke Regional Hospital, and Davis Ambulatory Surgery Center.*

Negin Saghafi, MD, DDS

- Arizona Oral and Maxillofacial Surgeons (private practice)

My journey toward dentistry started as a child when I spent time with my parents in their dental office in Iran. This was an easy and frequent arrangement, as my parents' office was downstairs from our flat, which made it a cozy and friendly environment, and the patients became like family. When I wasn't in the office, I would be playing in the backyard with my sisters. From time to time, we would be playing too loud and my dad would step out of the office to remind us to play quietly. As I got older, I started to become curious about the profession and learned more about the instruments. Soon, I could assist during procedures and became more drawn to dentistry as a career path.

When I was about ten years old, my parents visited my aunts in the US and decided to apply for green cards. They completed the application, but at the time had no definite plans to move. Eight years later, we received a letter from the American Embassy in Italy. The letter stated that we had missed our interview for the green card application and gave us the option to come in at an alternative date. This was an opportunity of a lifetime and came at the correct time, as my sisters and I were all transitioning from high school to college. Six months later, my older sister and I immigrated to the US.

Upon arriving in America, we moved in with my aunt for a few months until we found a place of our own. I was nineteen years old at the time and started taking classes at the local community college in Tucson, Arizona. I knew conversational English but studying in English was much more challenging. I had to have a dictionary on me at all times for constant referencing. Soon, my English improved and I started taking a normal course load and got an entry-level job to earn some spending money. After two years of studying at community college, I transferred to the University of Arizona and eventually graduated with honors as salutatorian.

While I was at Pima Community College, I took a Women's Studies class, where I was introduced to a work-study program that was geared toward involving female students in research. I was assigned a mentor and started working in a lab that researched fruit flies and cancer genes. These are the types of opportunities that would never happen in a country like Iran and I was eager to take advantage. I learned a lot through this program, particularly time management, and I also gained confidence in my own abilities.

I applied to multiple dental schools and got many interviews. My sister and I were accepted at A.T. Still University in Phoenix, Arizona and were planning to start dental school together. Phoenix was close to our new hometown, Tucson, and seemed like an easy and practical decision. However, I then got an interview at UCSF, and fell in love with the campus and San Francisco. Before long, I decided to move to California.

I was ecstatic to be at UCSF. I was very cognizant of the fact that I had started as a foreign student in a community college and now I was studying my dream profession at one of the best dental schools in the country. However, about the first week or so of dental school, I started to feel somewhat intimidated. I had never met so many people who were so smart in one place. In addition, the course load and amount of information I had to absorb was far beyond my undergraduate classes. At the same time, I enjoyed the challenge. I loved meeting new people and exploring new places in the city.

Beginning in my first weeks of dental school, anatomy was one of my favorite subjects and it showed. A few months into the semester, I received an email from our anatomy professor to inform me I had scored the highest in my class on an exam; he wanted to know if I was interested in tutoring anatomy. This may not seem important to many, but it was an important moment for me. It was a confirmation that no matter how difficult the work gets, if I want it and work hard for it, I can achieve my goal.

During one of the courses in the first year of dental school, we had a lecture from Dr. Schmidt, a prominent oral and maxillofacial surgeon and researcher. I can't remember exactly what topic he spoke about, but I remember I was amazed to find out how vast the field of dentistry could be. I had a few friends in the class ahead of me who were doing research in the oral surgery department and I began to speak with them about their work and oral surgery in general.

Before long, I was the only first-year dental student who was attending the weekly rounds on early Tuesday mornings. I was astonished by the head and neck cancer surgeries and the orthognathic cases and their effects on the patients' lives. I became sure oral surgery was the path for me after shadowing several cases in the operating room.

During the summer break, I applied for a research internship with Dr. Schmidt. He had already accepted another student, but he agreed to take me on as a second mentee. The research project was challenging and had many trials and tribulations. Nevertheless, I persevered and grew my research acumen, presenting my research at multiple conferences and even published a manuscript.

Toward the end of dental school, with application time approaching, I started to seriously contemplate my future career paths. From a professional perspective, I had a real passion for oral surgery, and I wanted to pursue a six-year, dual-degree program. From a personal perspective, I was engaged at the time and wanted to start a family and had concerns about what an oral surgery residency would mean for family life.

I spoke with many people, including my fiancé, my mentor, and my classmates from a year ahead of me about work-life balance. I vividly remember one day, during my externship in Eureka, California, I went on a long walk and thought for a very long time. By the end of that walk, I decided if I did not pursue oral surgery, I would regret it. Thankfully, my fiancé, who is now my husband, was very supportive of my ambitions. Therefore, I applied to oral surgery residency programs. After many interviews, I decided UCLA was the right program for me and was lucky to match there.

That summer, from June to July of 2011, I started a new chapter in every aspect of my life. I graduated dental school, got married the following week, moved to Los Angeles, and started my residency.

The first few days of residency were intense. As all interns, we were immersed in responsibility. Namely, we were in charge of the clinic and started taking calls on day one. However, I really enjoyed it and relished in the sense of accomplishment as I learned and progressed in my craft as an intern.

During my medical school years in the middle of my oral-surgery residency, my husband and I decided it was time for us to expand our family and have a baby after a lot of thought. We knew if we waited until after residency, fertility issues might arise as I would be thirty-five at that time. In addition, I understood having a baby soon after starting a new job presented difficulties. I met with my program director to let him know of my plans and he was very supportive. I was fortunate in that my plans for getting pregnant during the relatively easy years of medical school actually aligned with reality. I took off one eight-week block and resumed thereafter.

Many people talk about what a life-changing experience it is to have a baby. But still, I had absolutely no understanding of how much it would change my life until after my daughter was born. She brought so much joy to our lives. But it was also so challenging with two working parents with terrible schedules. My husband was a first-year medical student at the time, and he had his first exam on the day before our daughter was born. Furthermore, though our parents were very helpful for the first two months after I went back to work, they did not live in Los Angeles. So, it was a little bit like living on an island, at least in terms of childcare. We were fortunate to find a great nanny who helped us before and after daycare hours, since we both had long days. The year of general surgery was particularly difficult because of the extremely time-demanding schedule, replete with thirty-hour and overnight shifts. We endured with the help of the nanny, occasional visits from my parents, and the support of my husband.

Six years later, we decided to have another child after I had been working for a year in private practice. I thought I would be able to perfectly time this pregnancy and have no complications as was the case with my daughter. Unfortunately, I had a miscarriage during the week of my oral board exam. That loss was one of the hardest things I have ever experienced. But despite the emotional and physical burden this miscarriage brought to me, I passed my board exam and soon after I was pregnant again. This pregnancy was filled with complications and I was ultimately prescribed hospital bed rest for the last three months of it. I was lucky to have my husband and family's support—they took care of our daughter—and colleagues who were very accommodating with work coverage. Looking back, it is amazing to me what we endured, but we are happy to now have a happy and healthy five-month-old baby boy.

Being an oral surgeon is a long and winding road. Being a woman in oral surgery is even harder. Even though there have been many improvements in incorporating women into this male-dominant profession, it is still very much a work in progress.

I love being an oral and maxillofacial surgeon and am proud of the effort and grit it took to achieve my current position. I enjoy my daily surgeries and interacting with my staff and patients, and I like that we work as a well-organized team in my practice. This is often noticed by the patients, which gives them confidence in our ability to care for them. I enjoy helping people, whether it is getting someone out of pain or making an apprehensive patient feel more comfortable. I enjoy contributing to my community by doing charity cases and taking calls at the local hospital. In short, I feel lucky to provide needed care to patients and a guiding hand in the office. It is my eventual goal to move from associate to part-owner of my practice so I can further champion efforts to improve patient care and office dynamics, and help women break into oral surgery.

If I had to do it all over again, I would still choose to specialize in oral and maxillofacial surgery. My advice to my younger (and current) self would be to say "no" more often. I feel a great obligation to say yes to any opportunity, even if it leads to diminishing returns. As I grow older, I am focusing more on putting myself and my family first and saying "no" when I should.

Bio

Dr. Negin (Nikki) Saghafi is a board certified oral and maxillofacial surgeon, currently in private practice in Tucson, Arizona. She was interested in dentistry from a young age by observing her parents, who are both dentists. She was drawn to oral surgery during her dental school training because of its unique connection between medicine and dentistry as well as the potentially life-changing effects of surgery. She prides herself in providing excellent surgical care while being empathetic to her patients' needs.

Dr. Saghafi completed her undergraduate education at the University of Arizona, graduating with highest distinction, majoring in human physiology in 2007. She completed her dental school education at UCSF, distinguishing herself with multiple scholarships, involvement in research, and academic commendations, graduating in 2011. Dr. Saghafi completed her oral and maxillofacial residency at UCLA. She obtained her MD degree from UCLA, David Geffen School of Medicine as part of her six-year residency program. She completed a year of general surgery internship and extensive anesthesia training as part of her residency, providing her with the knowledge needed to provide the best care for her patients.

When she is not working, she enjoys spending time with her family, baking, cooking, hiking, and traveling. She enjoys learning new skills and is currently focused on pottery and crocheting.

Mona Stone, DDS

- Co-founder, RealHeroNeedsMasks— Instagram@stonesurgicalarts

- Social media activist and philanthropist

- Stone Surgical Arts; Westlake, Texas

I was only fourteen years old when my father was thrown in jail due to his religious beliefs back home. I remember vividly the night he was released. That was our last week in Iran. My parents had already had their house confiscated, again due to the systematic persecution back home like many other Baha'is (biggest religious minority in Iran). We left everything and packed and left for Austria. My life would never be the same from that point.

Whereas in the past my educational perspectives beyond high school were next to nothing (again due to the persecution against the Baha'is for allowing their children to take the entrance exam for university), now the sky was the limit. At that point I worked as hard as I could. While I was in college with a full ride scholarship at Washington University studying to be a bioengineer, I was working as a tutor in a local community college and as a cashier at Dillard's to make ends meet and help my family financially.

At the end of college, I was at a crossroads. I wanted to do something more; I wanted to make a big difference in the world and truly help people. I also wanted to live a lifestyle where my kids did not have to worry about finances. I met my mentor, Dr. Sclaroff, who is an OMFS at Washington University. I was amazed at his ability to repair facial fractures. Little did I know we would cross paths ten years later— that time when I considered becoming his associate and partner.

Life took me to many places in the world. Many things happened: dental school, internship, residency. In between, I constantly experienced sexism. I never allowed most of it to bother me; I was hard-headed and worked by principles and morals that were instilled in me at a young age by my parents. I would be lying if I said I never cried. Oh I did, plenty of times. Mostly in the privacy of my room. I still do from time to time. It is only natural. I will also tell you that sometimes I did put my foot down.

I was a third-year resident. He was my chief resident, a typical surgical resident with a gunner attitude. He and others had a grudge against me and the only other female resident. They made us do the scut work and gave us an extra call.

But one day things changed. I had been up all night operating. We were rounding on the medical floor with the remaining residents. He ordered me to check on another patient in the ICU. I picked up the phone to call the nurse. He grabbed my hand and took the phone from me, slamming it down as he proceeded to call me names. When he was finished, I didn't stay quiet like before. In front of all those doctors, nurses, and students, I pointed out how he was wrong and that his behavior was not acceptable. He never dared to treat me badly from that point.

The path to becoming a female surgeon is not easy.

Have I ever been given a week of extra calls just because? You know it.

Was I pushed out of a job situation when I got pregnant with my first child? I'll let you all answer that one.

For years, I have seen people, men and women, tearing each other up, bringing each other down. It started really in school with the competition to be in the top 10 percent of class to apply for OMFS residency, then in interviews. It escalated when I was in residency with upper-level residents literally making us feel worthless and questioning our abilities and intelligence. I was lucky my two amazing co-residents, both amazing surgeons, fathers, and husbands, were like me: easy-going.

But we all suffered. I got out and started to practice, where I experienced even more double standards being a female surgeon.

I also saw firsthand the ugly culture of competition for referrals. Some docs would literally do anything to get patients sent to them and sometimes their intentions when making treatment were, well, questionable. The sad part is that this still exists. It will not go away, however, if we nurture a culture of collaboration over contention maybe and only maybe we can change the course for some (or all) of our future professionals.

I am hoping we as a group of professionals, surgeons, and strong women can change the toxic culture—one essay, one blog, one book at a time.

Bio

Dr. Mona Stone is an esteemed oral and maxillofacial surgeon practicing full scope surgery, as well as an activist, philanthropist, and the co-founder of the grassroot organization, RealHeroNeedsmasks.

After receiving her dental degree from UMKC, she went on to do a year of internship at Truman Medical Center, followed by a residency in oral and maxillofacial surgery at Broward General Medical Center. She practices the full scope of the specialty, including maxillofacial pathology, dentoalveolar surgery, implant surgery, maxillofacial reconstruction, microvascular surgery, facial cosmetic surgery, and trauma. She is also an attending surgeon at Baylor Medical Center in Grapevine, Irving, and at Methodist Hospital.

Besides her role in the community, she is a mother of two beautiful toddlers, Max and Sofia. She's an avid supporter of motor sports and Formula 1, a TikTok creator, and a social media activist.

Suzanne Stucki-McCormick, MS, DDS

- Board examiner and Certificate Maintenance Section editor, *American Board Of Oral and Maxillofacial Surgery*

- Section editor, *International Journal of Oral and Maxillofacial Surgery* (IJOMS)

- President-Elect, American College of Oral and Maxillofacial Surgeons

- WOMENS LEADERSHIP INITIATIVE, https://www.omswli.com

Letter to a Younger Self: My Journey as an Oral and Maxillofacial Surgeon

Dearest Suzanne,

What an amazing journey this will be, filled with the highest of highs and some impressive lows. I will tell you the postscript now: all is well, you will be happy and fulfilled as you sure have done a lot of stuff.

Your interest in science begins at a young age. Your curiosity sparks you to take common household items, mixing them together along with colors from your paint set, to make a mini volcano of reds, blue, and green. Luckily, your parents don't get upset, and encourage your enthusiasm. By high school, you will enter the school's science fair, completing a project on dirt and erosion. This wins you first place at your school, as well as in your division for Northern California, and scholarship money for college. Winning in the science fair will afford you the opportunity of being only one of twenty high school students from the Bay Area to be selected to work at NASA, Ames Research Center. You are selected to work on projects involving brain mapping and DNA sequencing. Years later, you will realize these research projects teach you the scientific method: the sequential, logical approach to questions to be answered. This skill will serve you well in the more than 250 national and international lectures you will give, the fifty-six publications and book chapters you will write, and the three books you will author and edit. This skill will also serve as a method of how you will think about patients and their conditions, pondering "why not?" to allow your curiosity to move your career forward as well as your approach to patient care. Your patients are amazing and will become a source of strength; many will become lifelong friends. The bond of trust you will form with your patients is humbling, especially as you will travel to far off places to perform surgery for many whose language you do not speak well. Dedication and hope are universal.

But first, you are off to college, University of California at Berkeley, at the young age of sixteen. You're almost too young, so you have to learn how to adapt and get along, while standing up for yourself—another skill that will become useful later during OMFS residency training and as a young educator in New York. During the years at university, your interest in science continues. In your junior and senior years, you will be involved with basic science research projects at UC San Francisco, investigating Na+/K+ pump and ion channels associated with diabetes mellitus and in the summers you will spend time in the lab at Stanford University, evaluating blood flow through capillary beds in hamster cheek pouches. Yes, Susan, you are and always will be a nerd!

It is here that your interest in surgery will be sparked. Your neighbor and family friend is a famous cardiothoracic surgeon who allows you to shadow him. You self-identify with his philosophy of hard work, persistence, and believing in the vision of finding a solution when others don't think it is possible.

After UC Berkeley, you choose to obtain a master's degree investigating oral microbiology at West Virginia University. You had many choices for graduate study, yet call it chance or kismet, you choose Morgantown. Yet WVU is exactly where you will need to be, kismet for sure. You obtain a master's degree in molecular genetics, investigating Actinomyces, using a novel technique that will lead to DNA sequencing using PCA. You will meet your husband, a medical student, and marry. You will enter dental school and again in the summers be involved with basic science research, this time your own project investigating BMP, known then as AAA bone. Graduating from dental school with honors, you will become the first female ever to become a resident in the oral and maxillofacial surgery training program of WVU.

OMFS residency is a mixed bag. As your husband is also in residency training, several of his colleagues will be your chief residents, so in that regard your path will be easier. Yet, there are still many challenges in the form of comments and off-color remarks made throughout your training by faculty and residents alike. You will handle these with humor and style, especially as on most of your surgical rotations you are the only female and also often the first female on the team. Your favorite phrase in those situations will become, "Well, ain't that nice," spoken with a smile, which everyone knows translates into, "well, aren't you an idiot."

Ironically, the worst and most demeaning comments come from fellow OMFS residents. Often said as a quip or joke, from the very people who are your team, the ones you believe are your friends and have your back, they are the ones who judge you the most. Perhaps it is the proximity and closeness of hanging in the residents' room, or the hierarchical nature of residency training that allows these few persons to feel empowered to say the most deliberately unkind things. Do not take heed of these naysayers. Use your disadvantage to your advantage, and constantly move forward. They say that as a female surgeon, you are physically too weak to perform OMF surgery. Embrace your unique attributes. Don't mimic your fellow male residents, learn from them and work smarter, not harder.

The other challenge of residency training will come from family and friends. Even your well-meaning mother will wonder if surgery is the best choice, commenting, "Wouldn't you rather be an orthodontist? It's such a nice profession for a young lady." Yet she is a product of her time, not yours; no matter your choice, she will be proud of her daughter. Similarly, the long hours of residency training, and being "on call" will be brought up as lifestyle challenges. Yet this does not deter you. You will come to look back at the time spent during residency training as one of the best of your career, as the lifestyle of a surgeon will allow you to have the financial and time management freedoms to pursue your dreams for your life: family, volunteerism, and patient care. Women OMFSs will even advance to become highly sought after as partners in a practice, as they bring a unique perspective and value.

Hard work and the continued interest in research will allow you to present your research at almost every national meeting of the AAOMS, including as a first-year resident. That first meeting is memorable. The presentation is a success, which will lead to other opportunities for research and presenting your work at future meetings. Kismet intervenes again. It is through these scientific meetings, early in your residency, that you meet those who will be mentors and friends for the rest of your life. You will learn to lean on these friends and mentors. They are invaluable especially early in your career. You call them to celebrate your success. You also call them on those hard days, be grumpy and complain, saying, "I'm gonna quit"! Your mentors are wise and say, "Now Susan, you know if you quit, they win." With this sage advice, your determination will be renewed. Find mentors and rely on them. Later in your career, you will become a mentor to men and women throughout the world as well. One of your greatest support efforts will be on behalf of fellow female OMFSs and other women in challenging professions. Mentorship is essential to everyone's success.

During residency, you will develop an affinity for cleft lip and palate surgery, often volunteering to assist the only cleft lip and palate surgeon then in the region. You cannot imagine then where this passion will lead.

After residency, your hubby accepts a job as chair of pathology at the New York Eye and Ear Infirmary (NYEEI) in New York, so you two move to the big city. Unlike him, you have trouble finding a job. New York has so many OMFS residency programs that there is a glut of new graduates on the job market. You will find your way and in doing so forge a new path: a part-time position at Mount Sinai Hospital, part-time at NYU School of Dentistry, and NYEEI for academic practice. Kismet again and you are asked by two third-year dental students at NYU to help with a new research project. They had heard your lecture on TMJ conditions/surgery and wanted you to become involved with a new surgical procedure, distraction osteogenesis (DO). You take advantage of the access to Dr. McCarthy and the NYU craniofacial team's data set. You lay out all the radiographs on a long table and a pattern appears: DO is beneficial to the TMJ of children with craniofacial macrosomia and other dentofacial deformities. It is a pivotal finding and launches your research and academic career to the next level. As DO technique is in its infancy, overlapping in OMFS, ENT, and Plastics, you are soon involved in all three groups. Your research and novel clinical adaptation of the DO technique will flourish, resulting in travel all over the world, lecturing to academic groups, military academic groups, large seminars, and small groups. You will be attending meetings and cocktail parties as a peer, with the "who is who" of OMFS and craniofacial surgery, your idols, including the Pourquois-Pas group.

You will find yourself in amazing locales and wonderful places, including places you could never have imagined: St. Tropez; the Australian outback; and even standing across the "Blue Line" of the DMZ in North Korea with your colleagues after lecturing for the US military in Seoul, South Korea. And to think, you are still in your mid-thirties. You will also travel to Mexico to perform cleft lip and palate surgery, with the OMFS teams of Dr. R. Ruiz and the plastics team of Dr. F. Ortiz-Monasterio. Remember to pack your tennis racquet, as you will be playing doubles at his home while Mrs. Monasterio roots you on. You are on cloud nine.

Yet, nothing comes without a price. Your home life is under stress and divorce is the outcome. Eventually you will leave New York for another adventure: California. You will serve as professor and chair of oral and maxillofacial surgery at Loma Linda University (the second female OMFS chair in the US). It's an amazing opportunity and experience. From there, it's on to private practice outside San Diego, in Encinitas, California. Again, you will excel, and beach life in the sun suits you; you establish a unique private practice style, concierge in nature—a practice style afforded by a career in OMFS. You will become involved with Rotary International and work with a cleft team in Ensenada, Mexico in conjunction with the Department of OFMS at UCLA. You are recommended to apply to become a member of the Dental Board of the State of California and will serve for seven years and as president of the Dental Board of California for two terms. This will make you the first female OMFS to serve as president of a dental board. You will write and be awarded two patents for distractor/implants, the first female to achieve both. You will continue to be curious, taking training to become an ethics facilitator after becoming a fellow of the American College of Dentistry. This will lead you to author and edit a book on ethics for dental students. But that's not all; during your career you will serve on numerous committees for the AAOMS, the ADA, and CALAOMS; as trustee for ACOMS; and now as vice president of ACOMS. You will also serve on the Examination Committee as a board examiner for the American Board of Oral and Maxillofacial Surgery (ABOMS) and as Certificate Maintenance Section editor. Your passion for service to the profession extends to the international arena, serving on committees for the IAOMS, and now as section editor for the *International Journal of Oral and Maxillofacial Surgery* (IJOMS).

Respect for teaching will lead you to UCLA, and you will become involved with resident and undergraduate teaching at the dental school. So in essence it's full circle, yet much has changed. Surgery has evolved to become customized, with virtual surgical planning. Your passion now will evolve into evaluation of DNA for drug metabolism to customize medication protocols. You are also involved in education of the opioid crisis and developing best practices/ERAS for OMFS.

So, your path is exciting and extremely diverse. You will balance work/life challenges by always being curious, so nothing becomes a chore. Your lectures will allow you to travel all over the world, with close friends and family who will keep you grounded.

A career as an oral and maxillofacial surgeon was a wise decision for you. OMFS has given you the freedom and opportunity to follow your passion wherever it leads. Yet, make your choices wisely, with eyes wide open. No one comes through this life unscathed. Keep your heart open with kindness, caring, and a passion for life.

Bio

Suzanne U. Stucki-McCormick, MS, DDS, was initially in academic/ private practice in New York, where she worked with Dr. J McCarthy and Dr. Barry Grayson on the development of the distraction osteogenesis (DO) technique. She then became professor and chair, Loma Linda University and then moved to private practice in Encinitas, California. Dr. McCormick was appointed to serve on the dental board for the State of California and served as its president for two terms. She was the first female OMFS to serve as president of a state's dental board.

Dr. McCormick is currently involved with teaching at UCLA and teaching ethical decision-making in clinical practice with a focus on the national opioid epidemic. She serves as an examiner and is currently serving as co-chair of CM/CBT American Board of Oral and Maxillofacial Surgery (ABOMS). She also is section editor for the International Journal of Oral and Maxillofacial Surgery (IJOMS). She is currently serving as president-elect of the American College of Oral and Maxillofacial Surgeons (ACOMS).

"Not all heroes wear capes, some wear caps."
—DR. JACLYN A. TOMSIC

Jaclyn Tomsic, MD, DMD, FACS

- Attending, Case Western Reserve/UH OMFS

- Ohio's Center for Oral Facial Implant Surgery

- Instagram @doctorjacci

My path to oral and maxillofacial surgery was not linear. When I applied to dental school during undergrad, I had one thing in mind: to become a dentist and never be on call! I even remember saying out loud, "Who would ever want to do residency for six more years?! Not me!" Well, I could not have been more off key. During my third-year oral surgery rotation, I met Drs. Moore and Figueroa. They were oral and maxillofacial surgeons. I'm not sure I truly even knew what an oral and maxillofacial surgeon really was at the time, but they were fun and I could tell they loved what they did. At the same time, my true love for medicine and surgery also became apparent to me. So I took their advice and started to look into applying to oral and maxillofacial surgery residency. Fast-forward sixteen years and here I am: a dual-degreed, board-certified, fellowship-trained oral and maxillofacial surgeon. And I could not be happier with my decisions along the way.

I guess I can say now that I was subconsciously foreshadowing my own career with my above quote. When I realized OMFS was the career path for me, I also came to the realization that the six-year integrated residency and medical school track was the only one that would ultimately make me happy. I was truly fascinated with medicine and knew I had to accomplish this goal as well. So my path led me to complete four years of dental school in Boston; one year of hospital-based dental medicine general practice residency (GPR) in Charlotte, North Carolina; a six-year integrated MD OMFS residency program at the Detroit Medical Center/Wayne State University in

Detroit, Michigan, which included obtaining my medical degree from Wayne State University and completing a PGY1 intern year of general surgery; a one-year fellowship studying and correcting dentofacial and craniofacial deformity through orthognathic surgery, maxillo-mandibular advancement surgery for treatment of obstructive sleep apnea, and facial cosmetics under the direction of Dr. Jeffrey Posnick at Georgetown University in DC; a PGY2 year of general surgery at Washington Hospital Center in DC; and finally a one-year full scope OMFS fellowship in St. Louis, Missouri.

My training has allowed me to obtain a vast wealth of knowledge while also gaining invaluable life experiences, meeting and making lifelong friends and achieving academic success while having the opportunity to explore a number of amazing geographic locations. This last point is something I consider an immeasurable perk of higher education and medical/surgical training. Having contacts and networks all over the country has enhanced my ability to treat and refer patients and see the differences in treatment options and techniques across the country.

What I have discovered is a very unique specialty that blends surgery and medicine, my two passions, with dental medicine as well. I love the complexity and variety of cases I see on a daily basis and how, no matter where I am in my career, I am always learning. If I could tell my young self one thing it would be this: believe you will end up right where you are supposed to be. Try not to get too hung up on the little things that may put a wrinkle in your day. Life (and residency believe it or not) is too short. Oh, and to laugh a little and not be so hard on yourself.

My current passions within my specialty are orthognathic and trauma surgery. The focus of my fellowship was orthognathic surgery. I love this surgery because it not only provides satisfaction for me as the surgeon but is truly life-changing for every patient, providing such drastic function and cosmetic results. Similar yet so different, no two trauma cases are the same. I love how trauma surgery allows for the use of basic surgical principles to successfully diagnose, plan, and treat complex cases. I have most recently found a new passion as a residency program attending to not only educate, but also motivate my residents, students, future residents, and anyone who will listen to be the best they can be and help them understand the true gift we have as OMF surgeons to help our patients and our medical community. Finally, my goal is to increase the visibility of our unique and multi-faceted specialty and hopefully encourage and inspire other young minds—especially females—to pursue a surgical career.

The perfect fit for me is practicing full scope oral and maxillofacial surgery within a group private practice. I split my time between the office, the hospital, and staffing resident clinics as a part-time attending with an OMFS residency program. Practicing in a group allows for the availability of twenty-four/seven curbside consultations with my partners, sharing call and coverage for vacations and time off, built-in time to be in the OR, and working as a group to serve our community and promote OMFS—but most fun of all, the camaraderie we all share. Possibly the most fun and satisfying part of my job is working with the residents. They keep me on my toes and demand I stay up-to-date on my OMFS knowledge and literature. As an attending, I strive to create an open, easygoing environment to promote learning, education, and growth. I truly learn from them as much as they learn from me.

Choosing a career in oral and maxillofacial surgery has allowed me to have the best of all worlds, including work-life balance. As an avid sports fan, I am able to cheer on my favorite teams, either on the sofa or in the stands. I spend time volunteering and giving back to my community as a member of the Junior League. I round out my time enjoying travel, adventure, fitness, country music, and quality time with my significant other, family, and friends.

My three descriptives are detail-oriented on the job, first woman in my family to become a medical doctor, and loyalty—my friends and loved ones are my passion; I will do anything for them and cherish their friendship forever. Also a wannabe traveler and golfer.

Bio

Dr. Tomsic is originally and proudly from "The Land" (Cleveland, Ohio). She completed undergraduate studies at John Carroll University in University Heights, Ohio, where she graduated cum laude with a bachelor of science in chemistry and a minor in biology. She then attended the Boston University Goldman School of Dental Medicine in Boston, Massachusetts, graduating cum laude and earning her DMD doctorate. After graduation, she completed a GPR at Carolinas Medical Center in Charlotte, North Carolina.

Dr. Tomsic completed her oral and maxillofacial surgery training at the Detroit Medical Center in Detroit, Michigan. While in the "D," she attended the Wayne State University School of Medicine, receiving her medical degree from the largest single-campus medical school in the country. Dr. Tomsic then completed a one-year fellowship in jaw reconstruction, orthognathic surgery, facial plastic surgery, and sleep apnea surgery at Georgetown University Hospital in Washington, DC under the direction of Dr. Jeffrey Posnick. The next year she worked at Washington Hospital Center, completing her PGY2 year as a general surgery resident.

Dr. Tomsic relocated to St. Louis, Missouri, where she worked for five years as a full scope oral and maxillofacial surgeon at well-respected Mercy Hospital, a Level I trauma center. During her tenure at Mercy, she proudly obtained a fellowship in the American College of Surgeons in 2017.

She returned to Cleveland in fall of 2019, joining group private practice as well as the attending staff of the Case Western Reserve/ UH OMFS program and University Hospitals.

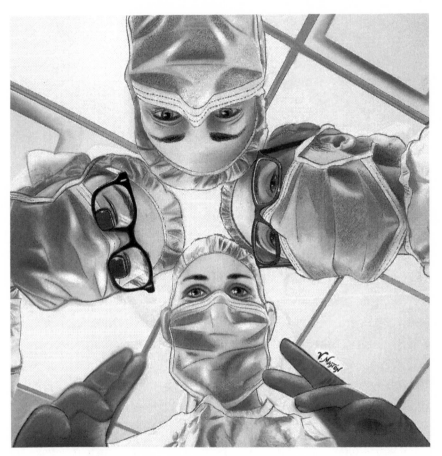

Dr. Chi Viet (right), then clockwise: Dr. Hunter Martin, Dr. Jessica Lee and Dr. Alyssa Loparich. These surgeons were co-residents at NYU.

Chi Viet, DDS, MD, PhD

- Attending surgeon and Assistant Professor at Loma Linda University, California

- Head and neck oncologic surgery

- Head and neck reconstruction; microvascular surgery

- Principal investigator of a translational research lab in head and neck cancer

My family immigrated to this country when I was five years old. My parents, previously professors at the dental school in Saigon, Vietnam, were forced to start over. Within a year of arriving, they were accepted into dental school in California. All three of us struggled to adapt to our new environment. My mother and father were now dental students, and I was a kindergartener who did not speak a word of English, in a class where I was the only Asian girl. Due to their time commitment at school, I was raised by my grandmother and aunt in Virginia, across the country from my parents. Although I was showered with love, I often wondered how much their career must have meant to them to be able to part with their daughter. Upon graduation, my parents opened an office. My father continued with his training as a prosthodontic resident, and my mother worked six days a week, often late into the night. And there I was, right next to her. I would sit in the lounge to read, and when I was older, around nine years old, went out to the reception to help with paperwork. I still remember one day when she left work before sunset. I was so ecstatic to see sunshine that it made my mom cry. My entire childhood was spent in this dental practice. So naturally when I went to college, I chose the career with which I was most comfortable— dentistry. I thought I would become a general dentist to take over my parents' practice. My parents couldn't be happier; they had so much love for this profession and were convinced their daughter would find as much fulfillment from it as they did.

Several experiences in my life shifted my career toward a different path. The first was my involvement in research. I initially started volunteering in an epigenetics lab at University of California, Davis, when I attended college, to become a stronger applicant for dental school. Shortly after starting, I realized I loved research. It required both thought and creativity to design experiments that could potentially solve mysteries of human disease. It challenged and fascinated me at the same time. For two years as an undergraduate researcher, I spent every available hour in the lab. When the time came to apply to dental school, I was torn—I knew I liked dentistry because I had been immersed in it since childhood, but research was a more exciting, albeit unpredictable, career. I decided to do both.

In 2006, I started dental school at University of California, San Francisco (UCSF) and immediately sought out research opportunities to continue my previous epigenetics work; I joined a lab focused on head and neck cancer. I started a research project to identify epigenetic biomarkers of head and neck cancer. To perform this work, I had to collect samples from head and neck cancer patients. My work with late-stage cancer patients transformed my clinical and research trajectory. I was moved by the challenges these patients endured. Most of the patients with whom I worked did not survive their disease, and most were beset with pain. One patient in particular was a recent immigrant from Vietnam with four young children. He had late-stage oral cancer, and by the time he came to see us, he was in so much pain he could not eat. I served as the Vietnamese interpreter during his appointments and felt a connection to him and his family. He died several months after our first meeting. I vowed I would become a head and neck surgeon to alleviate suffering in patients like him. At the same time, I wanted to perform research that could significantly impact disease outcomes in these patients. My enrollment into a PhD program, residency in OMFS, and all my subsequent research on head and neck cancer followed naturally from this decision.

I performed research while in residency, working in the lab during nights and weekends. Although the work required sacrifice, it provided me with an escape from the demands of clinical training. I found I needed the balance of research and surgery to feel content. I obtained my PhD during my intern year. The following year, I secured my first grant as principal investigator. After completing my PhD, medical school, and OMFS residency, and recognizing that success as a surgeon scientist required credibility in clinical and scientific realms, I completed a two-year fellowship in head and neck oncology and microvascular reconstructive surgery in Portland, Oregon. I was the twenty-seventh fellow, and the first woman to have completed the fellowship. Fourteen years after meeting my first head and neck cancer patient as a first-year dental student and watching how the disease consumed his livelihood and left his family in despair, I accomplished the goal I had set for myself—to obtain the surgical and scientific training needed to improve outcomes in these patients. Head and neck cancer is a capricious disease, and it has taken the life of many of the patients I have treated. Each time one of my patients loses to cancer, I feel as much sorrow as I did as a first-year dental student.

Aside from my patients who impacted my career path, I met several people during my training who changed my life. One of them was a research associate who collaborated with me on many of my projects. She and I became good friends. She later went to medical school but was diagnosed with a rare cancer during residency. Despite her poor prognosis after failing surgery and chemotherapy, she continued to enroll in clinical trials. Her sense of hope was striking, especially as she was a physician and knew her cancer was incurable. She was somehow able to accept her inevitable fate, but at the same time, remain hopeful. To her, being part of clinical research provided her with hope and gave her a sense of purpose that she could be helping future patients. Her passing deeply saddened me, but it reminded me of why I should devote my life to a career in cancer research, even knowing full well the path would be met with significant obstacles. I think of her often, especially in difficult moments of my career.

The second person I met was a friend in dental school who became the love of my life. When we first started dating, he told me he saw my passion for my career and he would do everything in his power to help me achieve my life's purpose. He has kept this promise through the years as a devoted husband. He moved around the country with me during residency and fellowship, and when I gave birth to our daughter as a chief resident, he became a wonderful and loving father.

Of course, it was the women during my training path who had the most significant impact on my career. The strong women in my family, from my mother to my aunt and grandmother, who had to rebuild their lives as immigrants in a foreign country, shaped my childhood and showed by example what could be accomplished with hard work. As a dental student going on OMFS interviews, I was surprised by how few women interviewees there were. At each program, I would often be one of two women—and undoubtedly the two of us would befriend each other and commiserate in our shared experience of being in the minority. Over the years, our chance meetings at these interviews blossomed into friendships. I was fortunate to match at New York University, a program where there were many women attending surgeons and residents. I did not realize how important it was to be in this inclusive environment until I graduated from the program. I rarely felt isolated because of my gender at NYU. To develop one's confidence and surgical skills in a place where no one thought twice about working with a woman surgeon was critical. To have mentors and co-residents who normalized being a woman in OMFS was what allowed me to become a mother during residency. Needless to say, it was with the support of these strong women in my residency and the friendships I developed during my training that made me the surgeon scientist I am.

Lastly, the one woman who had the most significant impact on my career path was Anh Le, DDS, PhD, the current chairwoman at

University of Pennsylvania. She is one of the few oral maxillofacial surgeon scientists in the country who has sustained a career straddling the operating room and an NIH-funded laboratory. I was introduced to her as a first-year dental student, and to my surprise, she spent quite a bit of time talking to me about what it meant to be a surgeon scientist. I later invited her to be on my PhD dissertation committee, and she agreed. Our research fields did not overlap, and yet her advice significantly propelled my PhD research forward. Similarly, while we never crossed paths in the same OMFS program, she was always there to mentor me throughout my training. Her frequent advice of, "be a good person, and the rest will follow," was often seemingly too simple and unrelated to any career obstacles I would tell her about, but it has become increasingly meaningful as I have progressed in my career. I have recognized the importance of fostering meaningful connections with people in my professional and personal life. With my collaborators, friends, and family, I aimed to be dependable and genuine in my interactions. It was not hard to do—it simply meant keeping my word on a project deadline, being present when they needed me, and focusing on how I could be helpful to them but not expect anything in return. That, to me, was the difference between networking and actually building strong relationships. Today, the majority of my research collaborations are with like-minded individuals who are exceptionally talented in their field, and who have chosen to work with me because of the deep connections we have fostered over the years. And, like the women before me who had spent the time to mentor me, I spend time to mentor my trainees. It is these meaningful relationships that drive my work.

If I were to go back in time, I would do it all over again. I encountered many struggles along my path that made me question whether the sacrifices were worthwhile. I missed many holidays and celebrations, lived across the country from my parents, as they had lived apart from me during their own training, and was at work when my daughter learned to crawl and walk in daycare. I often felt overwhelmed trying to reconcile my professional role as a surgeon scientist with my personal roles as a mother, wife, and daughter. However, in my darkest moments I relied on my family and friends, who offered empathy and love even when they knew that I was worn down and could not reciprocate. These struggles allowed me to grow as a human being and build stronger connections with those around me. Years ago, I made it my life's work to improve head and neck cancer treatment through research and clinical work. As daunting as the goal may have seemed, I have learned to take one step at a time, relying on my relationships as well as my own resilience to move past hurdles. While the dual time commitments at work and at home are not easy to balance, I have found a way to make it work for me and my family. During my two years in fellowship, my daughter and husband would routinely round with me on the weekends, after which we would spend time at the farmer's market and cook together as a family. To this day as an attending surgeon, my daughter often comes to work with me, sitting in the clinic or research lab. I suppose one day she will write about how she grew up at her mother's office, and I wonder if she will choose a similar path. Regardless, I hope to instill in her the importance of pursuing her life's purpose with authentic passion, building genuine relationships, and realizing that true wealth is measured by how much we give to others, not by how much we retain for ourselves.

Bio

Dr. Chi T. Viet is a surgeon scientist focused on head and neck cancer management. She is an assistant professor at Loma Linda University who earned her DDS and PhD from University of California, San Francisco, and her MD from New York University, where she completed her oral and maxillofacial surgery residency. She then went on to complete fellowship training in head and neck surgical oncology and microvascular reconstructive surgery in Portland, Oregon. As a head and neck oncologic surgeon, her practice is devoted to the comprehensive surgical management of patients with head and neck benign and malignant pathology. In addition to treating oral cavity and salivary gland tumors, she performs transoral robotic surgery (TORS) for tumors of the oropharynx. She is also specialized in reconstruction of complex head and neck defects using microvascular free flaps. She is devoted to improving disease outcomes for her patients and restoring their form and function through reconstruction of the face, jaw, and teeth after tumor ablation.

Dr. Viet is a principal investigator of a translational research lab focused on head and neck carcinogenesis and the neurobiological basis of symptoms faced by head and neck cancer patients. Her goal is to develop biomarkers for early head and neck cancer detection, and to use patient-specific biomarkers to design effective treatments for head and neck cancer and cancer-induced pain. By using patient samples, in vitro and in vivo models, she has demonstrated that epigenetic alterations are a common event in head and neck carcinogenesis. Her work on the role of epigenetics in head and neck carcinogenesis and cancer pain resulted in first author publications in Cancer Epidemiology, Biomarkers and Prevention, PAIN, PLOS One, *and* Clinical Cancer Research.

Dr. Rania Habib, pediatric cleft and craniofacial surgeon, performing an exam on a girl.

CHAPTER 5

Roadmap To Success: On Residency Applications

by Rania A. Habib, MD, DDS

"Patience, persistence and perspiration make an unbeatable combination for success."

— NAPOLEON HILL

You made the leap of faith to choose a career in OMFS, but now it is time to think about the best way to make yourself a competitive applicant. This takes dedication and hard work, but in the end it will be worth it. This list should help optimize your application.

Academics: Academics matter and to be a well-rounded oral and maxillofacial surgeon you need to understand all elements of dentistry. Make sure you dedicate time to studying *and* understanding all elements of every specialty in dentistry. This will help you understand the overall treatment goals of the patient. Do well on all your exams, classes, and board exams. Even schools that are pass-fail will often give honors or rank the top ten. Having an excellent class rank, GPA, and board scores helps you build your foundation as a strong dentist and therefore a well-qualified applicant.

Shadowing in OMFS: Shadowing an oral and maxillofacial surgeon is an important step in deciding if the specialty is the right fit for you and your lifestyle. It helps you to observe surgery and day-to-day obligations. If possible, try to shadow at an academic center, hospital, clinic, and private practice. This will help you experience the entire breadth of the specialty. It will also help you build relationships with surgeons who could serve as mentors or write letters of recommendation for your application.

Externships: Externships are usually a minimum of a week long and are typically scheduled at an OMFS residency program. This experience is usually organized by visiting the program's website and following the instructions to apply. Before applying, verify the number of externships allowed by your dental school and coordinate the timing, because each school may have different rules and regulations. It is a wise decision to schedule these early in your third year to get the experience before you decide to apply. For more information on available externships, visit https://www.aaoms.org/education-research/dental-students/oms-externship-opportunities or the program's website.

Externships serve three main purposes:

1. Exposure to residency training (call, stress, etc.) to help you live the life of a resident, which will help clarify if OMFS is a good fit for you.

   The last thing you want is to realize OMFS doesn't fit your lifestyle or mesh well with your life goals after you dedicate time and money to the application process. Plus, losing a resident puts a lot of stress on the program, especially the remaining residents, as it can prove difficult to fill an open position.

2. Exposure to the full breadth of surgical procedures, so you gain a comprehensive understanding of the full scope of the specialty.

3. Exposure to a residency program, which could help secure an interview at that program.

> If you are a standout extern, it may propel you to the top of the "must interview" list. On the flipside, a poor performance on an externship could propel you to the top of the "do not invite back for interview" list.

It is important to make a positive impression on your externship.

- Research the program before you show up so you know the attendings and current residents.

- Set up a meeting with the program director and/or chairman and come to it dressed professionally with copies of your CV.

- Learn to scrub before you do it in person to make sure you don't contaminate the field.

- On your fist day, show up early and dressed in professional attire with comfortable shoes and a crisp, short white coat. Bring a small bag with clean scrubs and operating room-appropriate shoes (non-permeable, closed toe, comfortable hospital shoes like Dansko, Berkenstock, Calzuro, Clove, etc.). If you choose to wear non-waterproof shoes, just make sure to wear shoe covers to keep them protected during surgery.

- Let your curiosity fuel you to prepare. Read about the surgeries you will observe before going to the operating room, focusing on relevant anatomy. This will help you understand the surgery better. During surgery, keep chatter and questions to a minimum so the surgeons can focus on the operation. Ask lots of questions when it's appropriate.

- Get as much hands-on experience as you are allowed, but also know your limitations. If you don't know how to do something, ask to be shown so you don't go rogue and create complications.

In general, have fun and make the most of every experience offered.

Comprehensive Basic Science Examination (CBSE): Since dental board examinations are no longer graded, the American Association of Oral and Maxillofacial Surgeons offers the National Board of Medical Examiners (NBME) Comprehensive Basic Science Examination (CBSE) as a tool for dental students to measure their understanding of basic sciences. This examination also serves as a tool for residency programs to evaluate applicants and it is now a required part of the application. For more information, visit: https://www.aaoms.org/education-research/dental-students/nbme-for-oms-applicants.

Each school determines the minimum score needed to apply to its program. Please visit the website of each residency program you want to apply to determine the average score needed and set this as your goal.

Application: The initial application for OMFS is centralized through American Dental Education Association (ADEA) Postdoctoral Application Support Service (PASS), https://www.adea.org/pass/.

This main application is created by PASS and sent to all the programs you chose. The application cycle generally opens mid-May and program application deadlines generally run from August–October. Most programs require a secondary application, so it is important to start early and stay organized. Try to submit your applications as early as possible because some programs give out interviews on a rolling basis, while others wait until the application deadline is complete.

The centralized PASS application requires the following submissions:

- Official dental school transcript
- Three to five letters of recommendation (Professional Evaluation Forms)

- Resume/CV

- Personal statement

- Institution Evaluation Form (IEF)

Letters of Recommendation: The centralized PASS application requires a minimum of three letters of recommendation but allows for two additional submissions. These letters are called Professional Evaluation Forms. You provide the e-mail. An electronic evaluation is sent electronically to your evaluator to complete. It is important to try to get these letters from oral and maxillofacial surgeons. OMFS is a unique residency and programs trust the opinions of fellow surgeons who understand the demands of the field. Early in your dental school career, try to establish these relationships so it is easy to find surgeons who can speak firsthand to your experience and character. Obtaining a letter from an externship is fine but understand this letter typically will not be as strong as a letter from your own program or local OMFS because that surgeon only knew you for a short time.

Personal Statement: This is probably one of the most difficult parts of the application to complete, yet it is a very important part of your application. This statement should focus on why *you* are the best candidate. It is an essay about you, not the specialty.

- Make it personal. Obvious, right?! Highlight the qualities that make you unique: your heritage, upbringing, key life moments, etc.

- How and when did you realize the specialty was your calling? Describe it in detail and make it unique to you.

- Avoid generic statements like, "Nothing beats the power of a smile," or "OMFS is the perfect blend between medicine and dentistry." We know this already because we are surgeons in the specialty. Don't tell us what we already know.

- What is your main reason for pursuing the specialty? What do you want to do when you finish—private practice, fellowship, academics, international work, etc.? It's also okay to not know yet and state that residency will help you make that decision. Know your *why*.

- Highlight your strengths but take the time to explain them. Answer why you are a team player, organized, etc. Use specific examples that demonstrate these qualities. It is not enough to simply list them.

- Do not describe the specialty. We know what our specialty entails. This is a statement for us to decide if *you* are a strong applicant. It is not the time for us to hear you gush about what we already know to be true.

Interviews: Now that you have made it to the program for the interview, this is your time to shine. Preparation is key. Practice interview questions with someone you trust to work on delivery.

- Research the program before the interview. Make sure you know the names of the attending surgeons and their surgical interests. Try to learn the names of the residents, but at very least focus on the senior residents who would be your chiefs. This small gesture helps you understand the makeup of the department and will also help you stand out.

- Dress professionally. A suit that fits your style is ideal. If you choose to wear a skirt or dress, make sure it is an appropriate length. Wear comfortable shoes because you may do a lot of walking if they offer a tour.

- Smile upon entry, shake hands firmly, and introduce yourself: "Hi, my name is _____. It is so nice to meet you, Dr. ____."

- Make eye contact. Looking all over the place gives the illusion of being aloof or absent-minded.

- Sit up straight; do not slouch or fidget.

- Remove fillers from your vocabulary: Like, um, oh, so, etc. Work on polishing your vocabulary and deliver your thoughts in full sentences void of fillers.

- Do not hesitate to pause to think about the question and then answer thoughtfully.

- There will likely be random questions meant to throw you off your game. Examples of these could include, "What is your spirit animal?" or "What was the last non-academic book you read?" These are meant to analyze how you work under pressure or in unusual circumstances.

- Do not feel obligated to answer questions that should *not* be asked in an interview. Examples could include, "Are you single or married?" and "Do you plan to have children during residency?" These questions are technically off limits, so smile and say something to force them to think about the question again like, "Sorry, could you repeat the question?" If they repeat it, try to answer in a respectful manner to keep the mood light, but remind them you know it's an off-limit question. Try something like, "Sorry, but I don't feel comfortable answering that question because I am not sure how that correlates with my ability to be a great resident."

- Create a written or computer spreadsheet or journal to keep track of the programs. They will all start to blend together, and you want to recall details that will aid you in submitting your rank list. Examples of things to document include: four versus six years; city; number of residents; average number of surgeries per year in each of the subspecialty areas: TMJ, cleft and craniofacial, oncology, head and neck microvascular reconstruction, trauma, esthetics, implantology; travel required to cover multiple hospitals/clinics; home versus in-hospital call; support of research; amount of vacation and do the residents say they actually get to take it; maternity leave; presence of female surgeons; OMFS board pass rate;

and resident happiness, overall vibe. You will spend four to six years at this program, so personalize this list to include things that matter to you. For example, I made sure there was an indoor rock-climbing gym within a thirty-minute radius from the main campus because climbing serves as my outlet to relieve stress, so this was an important factor for me when I applied and ranked my programs.

Resources

AAOMS for dental students: https://www.aaoms.org/education-research/dental-students.

ADEA PASS application: https://www.adea.org/PASSapp/Applying/.

Access OMFS blog: http://accessomfs.com/.

Life After Residency

by Rania A. Habib, MD, DDS

> *"Be aware that even before you have reached
> your ultimate professional destination, if
> you always strive for excellence, you can and
> should have a substantial impact on the world
> in which you live."*
>
> —SANDRA DAY O'CONNOR

After completion of oral and maxillofacial surgery residency, there are many options. You can choose to pursue a fellowship in a specific area of focus or go into practice. Most surgeons also chose to complete board certification. Let's take a closer look into the options post-residency.

Fellowships

OMFS offers many fellowships that allow you to focus your practice. If you fall in love with a specific subspecialty, apply early in your senior year (third or fifth year).

Check out: https://www.aaoms.org/education-research/oms-residents/oms-fellowship-opportunities.

- **Cleft and Craniofacial:** One- to two-year fellowship that focuses on head and neck reconstruction of congenital abnormalities or deformities. The focus of the fellowship will vary based on the program because some emphasize more cleft work and others more craniofacial. Most are pediatric focused, but since these craniofacial deformities span a lifetime, you may also treat adults. This ongoing care helps build a long-term relationship with these patients. Multidisciplinary care on a cleft team also helps optimize care, so most fellows will be part of the team at the host institution.

- **Head and Neck Oncology:** One- to two-year fellowship that focuses on the treatment of benign and malignant disease of the head and neck. Some fellowships are combined with microvascular reconstruction, which allows you to learn ablative techniques along with advanced reconstruction. Since a lot of cancer patients will require lifelong surveillance, this allows you to establish long-term relationships with these patients.

- **Microvascular Reconstruction:** One- to two-year fellowship that focuses on the reconstruction of the head and neck region. Some fellowships are combined with head and neck oncology to allow you to ablate the lesion and reconstruct it. Reconstruction focuses on the reestablishment of form and function using local, regional, and free tissue transfer to accomplish that goal. Most of these flaps require anastomosis (connection via suturing) of intricate blood vessels, so fine dexterity is key. Most will learn to harvest tissue (soft, hard, or combined) from all over the body to minimize morbidity while optimizing outcomes.

- **TMJ:** One- to two-year fellowship that may be combined with research. Oral and maxillofacial surgeons are uniquely positioned as the experts in the surgical management and reconstruction of the temporomandibular joint (TMJ). This fellowship focuses on expanding the surgical expertise with arthrocentesis, arthroscopy, total joint replacement, and combined TMJ/orthognathic cases.

- **Facial Cosmetics:** One-year fellowship that focuses on surgical and non-surgical head and neck rejuvenation.

- **Orthognathic:** Although most oral and maxillofacial surgeons have full competency in orthognathic surgery upon completing residency, this one-year fellowship allows additional focus on difficult cases, combined TMJ cases, and increasing efficiency.

Board Certification

The American Board of Oral and Maxillofacial Surgery (ABOMS) is the certifying board for OMFS and requires completion of two separate examinations. The certification process ensures graduates of an OMFS program have maintained a standardized professional credential and appropriate training, experience, and knowledge. Once board certified, the diplomate must maintain a certification maintenance process to retain the board certification designation. This ensures surgeons are maintaining a superior standard of care to protect the public and fosters lifelong learning.

Check out ABOMS's website for more information: https://www.aboms.org.

- **Qualifying Examination (QE):** This is a computer-based examination taken in the final year of residency or within the first few years of practice. It consists of 300 questions that cover the ten main areas of OMFS. Successful completion of this examination allows you to apply for the Oral Certifying Examination.

- **Oral Certifying Examination (OCE):** This is an oral examination taken after successful completion of the QE.

You have three consecutive years to take and pass it. This examination is a case-based examination administered by surgeons who are board certified and appointed as examiners by ABOMS. Upon successful completion of the OCE, you will become a diplomate of the board.

Job Options

Attending life is fabulous. Although residency and fellowship are extremely time-consuming and difficult, life after training is extremely rewarding. OMFS gives you the flexibility to find a job that fits your personality and lifestyle. The four main options for jobs are private practice, academic medicine, hospital-based position, and independent contractor, but you can tailor your job to combine these options. Most oral and maxillofacial surgeons will choose to take trauma calls, but the rigorousness of this call will depend on the level of acuity at the trauma center. Level 3 trauma centers are less demanding, while Level 1 trauma centers can be extremely busy during facial trauma calls. No matter the type of practice you choose, research, teaching, and volunteering can be incorporated into your practice.

- **Private practice:** Most new graduates chose to be an associate right out of residency or fellowship. An associate means you are employed by a private practice that could be owned by a solo surgeon, group practice, or corporation. In contract negotiation, there may be options to work toward becoming a partner in that practice. For those with a strong entrepreneurial drive, you can open your own private practice to focus on exactly the type of surgery you want to perform.

- **Academic medicine:** Entering into academic medicine entails being employed by a dental/medical school or OMFS residency program. This allows you to balance a busy clinical and operative practice while teaching. Depending on the contract, this may also require dedicating time to research to advance the field. Some programs may offer opportunities for surgeons in private practice to teach/supervise students or residents on a part-time basis, too.

- **Hospital-based practice:** Some hospitals that are not affiliated with an academic program may hire oral and maxillofacial surgeons as part of the hospital staff. This offers an excellent balance of clinical- and operative-based surgery. An advantage of this option is that the hospital is responsible for the maintenance and daily operations of your practice.

- **Independent contractor:** If you are interested in clinical-based surgery but do not want to maintain a practice or work for someone else, there is an option to become an independent contractor. You contract to work at various practices to deliver treatment but do not maintain an independent practice.

Pros And Cons Of An Oral And Maxillofacial Surgery Career

Pros:

- Interesting mix of oral, craniofacial, and head and neck surgeries

- Only surgeon who can administer anesthesia and operate

- Treat a wide age range of patients from infants to geriatrics

- Lots of opportunity for outreach in the local community and abroad

- Adjustable work-life balance based on the type of job you choose: private practice, academics, hospital-based, community clinic, etc.

- Excellent pay

- Variety of fellowship options to tailor your practice to your surgical interest

Cons:

- An overlap with other specialties that can create interesting hurdles—since OMFS spans dentistry and medicine

- Maintaining dental and medical licenses, including required CE for both degrees, if you are dual degree DDS/DMD and MD

- Rarely developing long-term relationships with patients, unlike other specialties in dentistry, unless you practice cleft and craniofacial, facial cosmetics, or head and neck oncology—once you complete surgery and they recover, you rarely see them back

- Reliance on obtaining patients via referrals, so it's important to create strong relationships with dentistry and medicine referrers—and establishing those relationships can be exhausting

Next, Dr. Justine Moe of University of Michigan will share her experience about residency application and her views on OMFS education and the training process.

Special Feature: Interview With Dr. Justine Moe

On OMFS Residency Preparation, Applications, And More

Dr. Justine Moe is a clinical assistant professor in the Department of Surgery, Section of Oral and Maxillofacial Surgery. She is the director of the Oral & Maxillofacial Surgery Residency and the Associate Director of Head & Neck Oncologic and Microvascular Reconstructive Surgery Fellowship. Read her story in chapter 4.

Below is a detailed interview with Dr. Moe on residency application and her own experience through training and as a faculty member.

Please list three things a female college student could do on her own time to explore OMFS.

- Contact and shadow an oral surgeon in practice. Consider shadowing an oral surgeon in private practice, hybrid practice, or academic practice. When spending time with the oral surgeon, ask a lot of questions.

- Contact and shadow a general dentist.

- Consider doing research with an oral surgeon. Choose a research mentor who has done research before and published. Discuss with the oral surgeon what type of project would be most interesting to you and most feasible in terms of time commitment.

Please list a few things a female dental student could do on her own time to explore OMFS/enhance their chances to be accepted into it.

- First and foremost, do well in dental school. Understand the value of knowing dentistry, as it is an integral foundation for oral and maxillofacial surgery. It is what sets OMFS apart from other surgical specialties of the head and neck.

- Spend time with the OMFS department at your home institution when you have free time. Apply for an Oral

Surgery Selective program if there is the opportunity at your institution.

- Spend time on externships with different OMFS programs to understand different healthcare systems and the scope of OMFS.

- Spend time with the OMFS residents. Ask questions and help however you can.

- Contact and shadow an oral and maxillofacial surgeon in practice. Consider shadowing one in private practice, hybrid practice, or academic practice. When spending time with the oral surgeon, ask a lot of questions.

- Consider doing research with an oral surgeon. Choose a research mentor who has done research before and published. Discuss with the oral surgeon what type of project would be most interesting to you and most feasible in terms of time commitment. Aim to present the research at a regional or national meeting and publish it in the future.

In your opinion, what are the three most important qualities an OMFS program director is looking for in a potential candidate?

- Integrity, curiosity to learn, and leadership.

- As a program director, I do not look for the individual who has the best hand skills or who I think will become the best technical surgeon. I am looking for an individual who possesses qualities that make him/her a humble and caring doctor who will do what is best for their patient, is able to be self-reflective and continually grow and learn throughout their career, and who promotes change and can lead.

- **Integrity:** This is the most important quality of a physician and surgeon. As physicians, we take the Hippocratic Oath, which states, "First, do no harm." Patients have entrusted their surgeon to make life-changing decisions with and for them every day, and it is of utmost importance that we act in a patient's best interest with every decision we make. Integrity is crucial as you go through training and allows those training you to safely teach you the art and science of medicine and surgery.

- **Curiosity to learn:** I want to train future oral surgeons who will love their profession, make the most of each learning opportunity during residency, and continue to advance themselves and grow throughout their career. Residency is such a unique opportunity to gain a broad exposure to oral surgery and other areas of medicine and surgery; staying positive and learning as much as you can will help get through challenging times and set you up for a successful career. There are so many changes in the field of oral surgery in the span of a few years; there are countless changes throughout your career. Maintaining a curiosity to learn and actively finding ways for self-improvement will help you continue to offer the best practices to your patients and lead to a more fulfilled career.

- **Leadership:** I want to train future oral surgeons who are proud of their profession, strive for advancement of the specialty, and not afraid of being the voice of change. Oral surgeons are leaders in many ways and there is no prescriptive way to be a leader. Some are leaders in communities, in healthcare institutions, in governing bodies, or through political advocacy. Some are leaders in research. Some develop new drugs, new technologies, or new devices. Some lead by teaching the next generation of oral surgeons. Some lead by outreach and bringing care to underserved individuals. I want to train future oral surgeons who want to change the specialty of oral and maxillofacial surgery for the better.

In your opinion, what are the challenges female candidates face when applying to an OMFS program?

- Lack of female mentors in OMFS to guide the candidate in the application and interview process

- Selecting programs to apply to based on perceptions of work-life balance

- Selecting programs to apply to based on financial obligations

- Selecting programs to apply to based on family constraints

In your opinion, how can candidates—male or female—stand out when applying for OMFS programs?

- Most importantly, be yourself at the interviews and highlight what makes you unique.

  The following are important considerations:

    - A strong academic record: Undergraduate and dental school records as well as CBSE performance are a good indicator of an individual who is able to learn medicine and OMFS in a fast-paced, busy residency program.

    - Strong letters of reference: Ask for reference letters from mentors who know you well and with whom you have spent a lot of time. Letters from an oral and maxillofacial surgeon if they know you well.

    - Good record of leadership, service, research, and teaching/mentorship activities: Make sure you highlight all the activities you do in your application.

In your opinion, how can we as a profession make the residents' experiences better?

- Improve what we do for resident wellness. Historically, surgical residencies have pushed trainees mentally and physically to the brink of what is humane. There have been many changes to improve residencies and protect trainees, including regulating work hours, changing workplace culture, and doing a better job of promoting wellness. There are, however, more changes that need to be made to improve the residency experience.

- In my opinion, these include:
  - Eliminate discrimination in programs and challenge implicit gender biases that affect program culture
  - Embrace non-traditional training paths that may allow for better work-life balance and achieving professional goals, i.e., allowing interested residents to complete dedicated research time during residency
  - Decrease program reliance on residents as service providers and shift the focus to education, which would improve work hours and give residents time to focus on learning
  - Standardization of maternity, paternity, and parental leave for residents across programs
  - More women in leadership positions, so female residents have mentors at all levels of leadership in OMFS
  - Better assessment of trainee wellness and implementation of systems to promote wellness

In your opinion, what are the top three reasons why a female dental student would **not** pursue OMFS?

- Lack of female mentors in OMFS
- Perceptions of work-life balance
- Financially unwilling to take on more debt or delay paying off debt

How do you think we could increase applications from females to OMFS programs?

- Improve visibility of female OMFS

- Increase mentorship opportunities between female OMFS faculty/practitioners and dental students

How difficult was it to prepare for the board examinations being pregnant or raising children during residency and working full time?

Throughout all stages of your professional career, work-life balance is an active process and one you need to be intentional about. Balance is also different for different individuals. You need to identify what compromises you are willing to take and what is important for you to be present for.

What I do:

1. I personally live by my Outlook calendar. All of my meetings, appointments, and surgeries are on the calendar. I also schedule time for working out, family time, and research time, so my family and those I work with know these cannot be compromised.

2. I try to bring my professional and personal lives together when possible. I bring my child into the office occasionally and am able to get work done while giving her a richer experience and allowing her to understand I have roles other than being a mother that are important and fulfilling.

3. I outsource and use help. I see value in spending money to gain time. I use a house cleaner, lawn mower, snow removal service, and landscaping service. I have a nanny as well. This reduces the time I use for tasks like those.

4. I make time for family and friends and make sure I show my appreciation for them—because family or partner support is so important.

Would pursuing further fellowship training change your decisions of whether to get married and/or have children or vice versa?

No. I am a head and neck fellowship-trained oral surgeon. I completed a six-year OMFS program after completing a GPR and an oral surgery internship. I got married during my fellowship year and had my first child during my first year of practice. During my first year of practice, I was not only pregnant and then on maternity leave, but also was a top RVU earner in my practice. Regardless of the path you take, you can achieve work-life balance, and there are challenges with work-life balance if you are in dental school, residency, fellowship, private practice, or academic practice. Do life as it happens and when it is right for you; do not let your work dictate other life choices. Support from your partner, family, and friends is very important during all stages of your professional career.

Would you suggest a specific roadmap or path to get to where you are today?

I don't know if there is a specific roadmap. There is nothing wrong in taking an unconventional path to a career in OMFS rather than going to dental school after college and applying for OMFS residency during dental school. A variety of life and professional experiences can make you a well-rounded oral surgeon and professional.

How do you think women oral and maxillofacial surgeons in practice can contribute to encouraging young women to enter the specialty of OMFS?

Be involved with a dental school. Mentor dental students who are interested in oral surgery. Invite undergraduate and dental students to shadow in your practice.

You are currently a full-time faculty member; how long is your total education plus training thus far, and what is your current position?

My total education is fifteen years, including four years of dental school, one year of GPR, one year of OMFS internship, six years of OMFS residency, one year of head and neck oncology/microvascular surgery fellowship, and two years of academic practice. I am currently the residency program director at the University of Michigan. I am also a clinical assistant professor, as well as associate fellowship director of head and neck oncologic surgery.

Have you seen any trends or changes in the female applicants and residents over the span of your teaching career? What can you do/ have you done personally to encourage more applications from female dental students? Also, what has been done in your institution that you find to have positive effects in supporting female residents or students?

In the last two years as a faculty member, there has continued to be a small percentage of female applicants to our six-year OMS program. At the University of Michigan, we developed the Women in OMS symposium, held for the first time in March 2018 and again in March 2019. This symposium was designed with the aim of providing a platform to discuss unique opportunities and challenges faced by female OMS throughout their career. The 2019 conference focused on skill building in leadership, conflict management, and career development. We discussed barriers to the advancement of women in OMFS and strategies to meet these challenges. The 2019 symposium was attended by dental students, OMFS residents, dentists, dental personnel, and OMFS practitioners in academic and private practice from across the US, Canada, Mexico, and internationally. Through this symposium, we developed a network of female dental students, residents, and practicing OMS for mentorship and sponsorship. We plan to continue this symposium for years to come.

We are intentionally working to change and cultivate a culture of individuality, inclusivity, and wellness. This has allowed open conversations between trainees and faculty and opportunities to better identify challenges and come up with ways to support resident wellness.

CHAPTER 7

Women and Leadership

"As a country and as a world, we are not comfortable with women in leadership roles. We call little girls bossy."

—SHERYL SANDBERG

What is leadership to you? Let's examine leadership by finding out what leadership is not. Diana Booher, MA, of Booher Research Institute, Speaker Hall of Fame, in her 2015 *Huffington Post* article, pointed out three things leadership is not.[44] "First, leadership is not position, but rather personal influence. Second, leadership is not power, not simply granted but earned. Last, leadership is not pride, and the greatest leaders demonstrate deep humility."

Women continue to strive for equality and equity over the past decades across different professions. However, in certain doctrines, women continue to remain to be the minority in number. When we examine the business world, according to *Harvard Business Review's* Women and Leadership,[45] women in the workforce now occupy

---

[44] Dianna Booher. *"3 things leadership is not"*, September 2016. Huffpost. https://www.huffpost.com/entry/3-things-leadership-is-no_b_8179546

[45] Alice H. Eagly and Linda L. Carli. *"The Women and the Labyrinth of Leadership"*. On Women and Leadership, HBR's 10 Must Reads. 2019. Pg. 3

more than 40 percent of all managerial positions in the US. However, within the C-Suite, meaning those with titles chairman, CEO, CFO, for example, only 6 percent are women. An article in the book by Alice H. Eagly and Linda L. Carly, *The Women and the Labyrinth of Leadership*, points out that "women's leadership style—characterized by innovating, building trust, and empowering followers—is ideally suited to today's business challenges." Many, if not all, healthcare facilities such as hospitals, surgi-centers, long-term care facilities, and private practices, are for-profit businesses. Surgical specialties, in particular, employ lower numbers of women, mostly due to their traditionally longer and rigorous training. Therefore, it is important to cultivate women's leadership skills from not only a clinical perspective, but a business perspective as well. I would reckon the C-Suite could stand for Clinical-Suite for us surgeons.

When I attended the Women Dentists Leadership Conference at 2019's Greater New York Dental Meeting, one of the speakers, Dr. Theresa Gonzales, a retired colonel of the US Army and the executive director of the American College of Dentists, presented statistics of women in the military. According to the presentation, in 2009, women comprised 8 percent of the total veteran population in the US and are projected to reach 15 percent by 2035. As of 2015, women made up about 15 percent of the US military. I reached out to Dr. Gonzales after her presentation to share the similar statistics for women oral and maxillofacial surgeons; at the time, there were only 8 percent female AAOMS members and 16 percent female residents in training. Dr. Janice Lee's August 2019 *JOMS* article, "From Ripples to Mavericks,"[46] mentioned that she wished to see 30 percent women in OMFS by 2030. The "thirty by thirty" goal will require a concerted effort from all directions to promote women to leadership seats, not merely tokenism. But first, we each need to understand what leadership means to us, as we may ultimately cultivate different leadership styles.

---

[46] Janice S Lee, Barbara L Bass, Pamela J Hughes, and Alison Davis-Blake. "From Ripples to Maverick." *JOMS* 77(8) (2019)1532-1533

The Importance Of Leading Yourself And Finding Your Uniqueness

Historically, leaders in their respective fields share certain characteristics. Rebecca Halstead, a retired brigadier general of the US Army, in her book *24/7: The First Person You Must Lead Is You*,[47] identified six leadership competencies: decisive, assertive, independent, friendly, unselfish, and caretaking. Although she identified the first three characteristics as being more "male" and the last three as more "female," she further claimed, "we, men and women, need to focus on simply understanding the basics of great leadership, which is not about gender."

In a way, you can draw several parallels between residency training programs and military training, in that discipline, focus, mental and physical toughness, and hierarchy exist in both. I could say what was described as the general mentality at West Point as "to cooperate and graduate"[48] also applies when it comes to surgical residency. In her book, Halstead noted even at five-feet-one-and-a-half-inches tall, she once surpassed a male fellow soldier on the Zero Day, which was an obstacle course. Her male colleague, upset about being defeated, confronted her, as he was focusing on beating the woman cadet. She replied she wasn't thinking of surpassing him, but the importance of reaching her "PB"—personal best.[49]

Two principles in this book especially stood out for me: one is "you must choose the harder right over the easier wrong,"[50] which is about personal integrity—to make the right decision no matter how difficult. The other is "be authentic: stay real and humble."[51] Tom Ziglar, the son of Zig Ziglar, also said leaders must have integrity, which leads

---

[47] Rebecca Halstead. "*24/7: The First Person You Must Lead Is You*", CreateSpace Independent Publishing Platform. 2013, Pg. 62.

[48] Rebecca Halstead. "*24/7: The First Person You Must Lead Is You*". Pg. 77.

[49] Rebecca Halstead. "*24/7: The First Person You Must Lead Is You*". Pg. 62-63.

[50] Rebecca Halstead. "*24/7: The First Person You Must Lead Is You*". Pg. 19.

[51] Rebecca Halstead. "*24/7: The First Person You Must Lead Is You*". Pg. 66.

to trust, and the best way to lead is through vulnerability.[52] To me, vulnerability is a component of being authentic. To be vulnerable is to not to be afraid to show fear or concerns, or to admit to mistakes. To be vulnerable is not needing to be the "good guy" all the time. It is important to recognize that learning how to be vulnerable is a brave act, and not weak by any means. As surgeons, we've been taught to stand tall, work under extreme pressure, and not complain (suck it up, buttercup) as our default mode. However, at times of distress, sharing genuine concerns with your team members by keeping it real will help create organic connections and cohesiveness within your team.

I am naturally soft-spoken. And although considered of average height in my native country, I have been told countless times that I am considered "little" or "petite" in the US and I look young, which makes me seem less like a dentist, a doctor, or a surgeon. I recall when I did my anesthesia rotation as a first-year resident, during one of the cases, the plastic surgeon turned around and saw me behind the curtain. He popped his eyes and said slowly in his Barry White deep voice, "Do your parents know you are here?"

I definitely went through an identity crisis when I started the residency. Should I act like one of the guys? If I don't, then what? I learned over the years that I needed not to dress like a guy or act like a guy to perform my daily tasks. When I first opened my practice, I went to visit a general dentist in my neighborhood. He looked at me from head to toe, up and down, and sneered, "What is a little girl like you doing here?" I was thirty-six years old. I just passed my board exam. I was a mother of two, and a new practice owner. "Little girl" was certainly inappropriate to describe me. Comments like those could be quite deflating sometimes. However, when you doubt yourself and feel you need to fit in by being anyone other than your true self, know that when you learn to be comfortable in your own skin, it is then that you can achieve your personal best. Caroline Nuttall, VP of Forbes Books and one of my business coaches, in her

---

[52] Tom Ziglar E-Newsletter, 2021.

signature talk "Find your unique fishy-ness," used the toothpaste aisle in the supermarket as an example. She said this aisle gave her anxiety, as all the toothpaste looked the same. How do you know which toothpaste is best for you in the toothpaste aisle (being a non-dentist)? Which toothpaste stands out? She emphasized the importance of finding your unique qualities to stand out in the sea of sameness, what she calls "your unique fishy-ness."

The Challenges Of Being A Woman Leader In A Male-Dominated Field

When you choose a surgical career in oral and maxillofacial surgery, you also inevitably choose to become a leader, regardless of whether you decide to work in a private practice or a teaching institution. In the process of pursuing residency and even fellowship training, you will learn to make independent decisions, give directions to your junior residents, follow leads from your senior residents and attendings, and take responsibility and accountability for your actions. Being a woman in a residency full of men need not be a disadvantage but an additional advantage of developing leadership qualities; you will learn to communicate effectively regardless of gender. When application committees examine two potential candidates with similar credentials, would being big and tall, being the male gender, and perhaps being Caucasian be more convincing to fulfill the imagery of a traditional leader? Certainly, a charismatic, eloquent personality may seem to be the icing on the cake. However, if we do not fulfill these seemingly important external criteria of a leader's image, does it mean we are disqualified to being a future leader? How did women cultivate themselves as leaders earlier on?

There Is Only One Tony Robbins

Susan Cain, author of *Quiet: The Power of Introverts in a World That Can't Stop Talking*, discussed the "myth of charismatic leadership," of how we see "quick talkers as more capable and appealing than slow talkers."[53] However, research shows no correlation. She further pointed out that many effective CEOs are introverts, including Charles Schwab, Bill Gates, and Brenda Barnes.

If Tony Robbins would ever submit a CV, I imagine it reads: *I am Tony Robbins and there is no one quite like me.*

As a dentist, a doctor, a physician, and a surgeon, we do not interact with our peers or our patients by jumping up and down and yelling in over-exaggerated heightened excitement to provide excellent care. We need not to be extroverts to succeed. In fact, many scholars and researchers are introverts. In 2018, I attended a Cal Alumni lunch to meet with former Secretary of Defense Norman Mineta and his wife in Philadelphia. It was an intimate group lunch and most attendees were Asian. One particular Caucasian man who was a quick and loud talker, a classic extrovert, would constantly monopolize the conversation and interrupt others. I observed that the group adhered with the unspoken cultural code of politeness to slowly allow the conversation to evolve around the table. I also observed that Mineta would politely redirect his attention to the rest of the group and ask to get to know everyone while this man would continue to interrupt, unaware he was being rude.

This man's behavior reminded me of a certain senior resident who would command through overpowering others with his speech pattern that was quick, loud, and intrusive. He was also big and tall. As a young woman, I used to be intimidated by people with personalities like that. However, over the years, as I was developing my own leadership style, I realized dominating speech in a group did not translate into true leadership.

Don't Cry, Don't Yell: Where Is My Scut Monkey On Leadership Training?

In the book, *Being A Woman Surgeon: Sixty Women Share Their Stories*,[54] Dr. Sarah Blair, surgical oncologist, described the two most

---

[53] Susan Cain. *Quiet. The Power of Introverts in a World that Can't Stop Talking,* New York, NY: Random House, Inc. 2012, 2013. Pg. 51.

[54] Preeti R. John, ed. *"Being A Woman Surgeon."* Los Angeles, CA: Gordian Knot Books, 2015, Pg 137.

common categories of women she encountered during residency in the early nineties were the criers and yellers, or both. She described the yeller as the "dragon lady" and the criers who cry or blame when things went wrong.

Oftentimes, academic excellence does not necessarily translate into leadership skills. In school, students focus on achieving high merits without being trained on leadership skills. Most intensive studying requires solitude and what Cal Newport called "deep work,"[55] which is defined as "professional activities performed in a state of distraction-free concentration that push your cognitive capabilities to their limit." Studying for exams in dental school and medical school is deep work. Studying for the board exams is deep work. Performing surgery is definitely deep work. You might exclaim, "I want to be a surgeon!" You apply and match a surgical residency program and soon learn to survive a hierarchical architecture where interpersonal communication and leadership skills are crucial to success. An intern, when first starting residency, may be advised to "do as you are told" and "don't speak unless you're spoken to." Residents follow traditions of "how it's always been done" without receiving actual leadership training. Just follow the ladder and you will be granted more privileges when you get there. That is positional leadership.

Hippel et al. discussed female communication styles and stereotype threats.[56] Society accepts male communication styles as associated with leadership qualities. Female communication styles result in women often being viewed as less competent as leaders. Women, when faced with stereotype threats, often react by adopting male communication styles (try to act like a man). However, the consequences are social penalties: women being viewed as less kind and aggressive. As women, we might at times feel we must overcompensate for our physique and appearance to command

---

[55] Cal Newport. *Deep Work*. Grand Central Publishing, 2016. Pg. 3.

[56] Coutney von Hippel, Cindy Wiryakusuma, Jessica Bowden and Megan Shochet, "Stereotype Threat and Female Communication Styles". *Pers Soc Psych Bull* 37 (2011): 1312.

by becoming a yeller, and then when we are finally emotionally, physically, and mentally overloaded, we inevitably become criers. You ask, where is my scut monkey on leadership training?

Understanding communication styles and differences in communication are key to integrating yourself with your team. Residents from different backgrounds are cherry-picked into the training program based on overall academic excellence and potential for high performance. Residents are expected to work closely together as an efficient, functional team. However, since each person is unique, our gender, age, sexual orientation, religious beliefs, country of origin, and political views may all vary, with personal conflicts inevitably arising due to individual differences. Conflict resolution skills then become a vital part of leadership training. As more training programs evolve to accept more female residents who in turn may become future female attendings, a shift in group dynamics is expected to happen as time goes on, shifting from a traditionally male-leading-male group dynamic that can very well be top-down, to male-leading female, female-leading-male, or female-leading-female, or a combination of group dynamics. More efforts should be geared toward developing communication skills that are gender-neutral and goal-oriented.

In *HBR's* ten must reads On Women and Leadership, different linguistic styles and their consequences were discussed.[57] Early socialization determines how little girls play differently from little boys, where "girls tend to learn conversational rituals that focus on the rapport dimension of relationship whereas boys tend to learn rituals that focus on the status dimension." It was described as "girls downplay ways in which one is better than the others and emphasize ways in which they are all the same, while boys learn to use language to negotiate their status—giving orders is one way of getting and keeping the high-status role." Therefore, when women use more "we" than "I," acting modestly by downplaying, avoiding challenging others' ideas, and apologizing too freely, these behaviors

---

[57] "On Women and Leadership." HBR's 10 Must Reads. *Harvard Business Review*. 2019.

are interpreted as a lack of authority when interacting in a men's circle. Avoid "uptalk" when communicating. Read books that will help you to improve communication skills early on in your career.

Cultural Context In Communication: It's Not Personal

I learned in my early career not to take things personally. It took some time to get there. This was especially hard, as many aspects of residency training were opposite to my cultural beliefs as an East Asian of Confucius philosophy; I was raised to be humble and respectful and allow others to express their opinions first. In a Western society, especially residency, it was viewed as a lack of authority and passiveness. In my culture, "saving face" is important—not having the last word, and not pointing out someone else's mistakes bluntly, especially in public.

Developing thick skin comes with time and once I knew to let go of the ego to just stay with the facts, it helped me look at the bigger picture to achieve my goals without worrying about being rejected, and just keep propelling forward. In my book, *Pulling Wisdom: Filling The Gaps Of Cross-Cultural Communication For Healthcare Providers*, I shared personal experiences as a first-generation immigrant learning English and being exposed to different cultures in America, and how I adapted to become a better communicator with people from different cultural backgrounds over the span of thirty years.[58]

"I Dissent"/The Notorious RBG: Challenges As A Woman Leader

On September 18, 2020, the well-respected Justice Ruth Bader Ginsburg, known as "the Notorious RBG,"[59] the second woman on the US Supreme Court and the first woman to hold the tenure position at Columbia Law School, lost her battle with cancer. In a

---

[58] Cathy Hung, *Pulling Wisdom: filling the gaps of cross-cultural communication for healthcare providers.* (Charleston: Advantage Books, 2020)

[59] Ruth Bader Ginsburg: *The biography.* (Middletown: University Press, 2020)

time when diversity and inclusion did not yet exist, being a Jewish woman who was a mother put her at a disadvantage to land jobs at private firms despite her immaculate academic record. She had undoubtedly mastered the art of negotiation when it comes to leadership development in her linguistic styles, and yet, she had to wear loose clothing during her second pregnancy due to fears of getting fired. She was the perfect example of overcoming adversity in the era of racial and gender inequality. She fought for cases where women were denied because of gender. She was a progressive force who grew up in a household of two working parents, married a supportive spouse who treated her as intellectual equal, and gained respect in a male-dominated profession of law. She did not try to fit in or dress like a man. She stayed authentic to her cause on gender inequality issues while staying in a high-power leadership seat.

Be A Transformational Leader: Inspire And Motivate

The concept of transforming leadership, first developed by James MacGregor Burns,[60] states, "leaders and followers help each other to advance to a higher level of morale and motivation," a "give and take" relationship. This is opposed to "transactional leadership," where a leader influences others by what they offer in exchange, like a transaction, instead of motivation. There are four elements in transforming leadership: individualized consideration, intellectual stimulation, inspirational motivation, and idealized influence. In other words, positions and titles are irrelevant, and in addition to teaching the technical and theoretical aspects of the doctrine, it is also important to inspire and motivate. Hippel et al. in *Stereotype Threat and Female Communication Styles*[61] recommends female leaders adopt a transformational leadership style, which creates a "female leader advantage." Check with your school or residency program to see if there is a leadership or mentorship program available. Look outside the industry for leadership programs and do your due

---

[60] James MacGregor Burns. *Leadership.* (HarperCollins Publishers, 1978)

[61] Hippel, "*Stereotype Threat and Female Communication Styles.*", Pg. 1312

diligence. This goes hand-in-hand with the mentorship program: Be a mentee, then a mentor. Start a GoFundMe campaign for a good cause. Volunteer in organized dentistry or medicine. Speak out or write a blog. Start a club and conduct seminars. Start a page or a group on social media. Leadership is not about position or status, but influence, with objectives, as I learned from Dr. Ashleigh Rosette of Duke University Fuqua of Business, during my training at the Institute for Diversity in Leadership. In other words, how would you like to impact others and what are your objectives? See the Resources section for a list of my personal favorite leadership books.

The Importance To Develop Organic Connection By Being Yourself

In *Authentic Gravitas: Who Stands Out and Why,* author Rebecca Newton describes the most central components to leadership and professional success as intent, which is the kind of leader or professional you want to be, and impact, the legacy you want to leave.[62] She further stressed the importance of developing your "personal footprint" to connect with people by being intentional. She clarified that people who have "gravitas" bring value, rather than those who are merely charming with charisma.

Step Out Of Your Comfort Zone And Network

The idea of networking can be intimidating to some; at professional conferences where meals are served, whether buffet style or plated, I've noticed there is often an unspoken, volunteered social distancing even before COVID. I might conveniently place my pocketbook in the seat right next to me, or the gentleman next to me skips a seat, instead of sitting right next to me. In a round table seating eight people, it is not uncommon to see two or three skipped, empty seats. Many professionals are naturally uncomfortable with feeling the need to actively network or socialize. "I am here to get

---

[62] Rebecca Newton. *Authentic Gravitas*. New York: Penguin Random House. 2019. Pg. 11.

my continuing education, that's all. I don't feel like talking to anyone right now," you might say. Your inner voice says, "I don't see how I can have anything in common with this person." Occasionally, someone would strike up a friendly conversation, and more often than not, I found through sharing I had many things in common with the stranger who made an effort to talk to me.

Networking with your colleagues is of ultra-importance for any professional. You might find true friendship, opportunities to collaborate on projects, tips on practice management or clinical courses, or simply the name of a great restaurant in town. More often than not, when I start conversations with people sitting right next to me, there are always things to be shared. As I write this, COVID-19 still impacts our daily lives and most, if not all, in-person conventions or meetings have gone virtual. Social media such as Facebook, LinkedIn, Twitter, and Instagram can connect you to thousands of people easily. If you are more comfortable behind the screen, use the power of social media to connect and learn from others. One thing I can't emphasize enough is that a successful career involves support from men and women. Women's leadership does not mean a tug-of-war with male colleagues but learning to collaborate through different communication and leadership styles.

The book, *Navigating Your Surgical Career: The AWS Guide to Success*, published by the Association of Women Surgeons,[63] has a chapter on networking and professional development for further reference.

Are You Calibrating Your Ceiling?

Amelia Earhart, the first woman to fly solo across the Atlantic, was born around the turn of the 19th century.[64] Aside from my personal curiosity of how she might have functioned with her sinusitis in a

---

[63] Susan E. Pories, MD, FACS, Nancy Gantt, MD, FACS, Christine Laronga, MD, FACS, and Dixie Mills, MD, FACS. eds., *Navigating your surgical career: the AWS guide to Success* (Chicago: Association of Women Surgeons, 2015)

[64] Doris L. Rich. *Amelia Earhart: a biography.* (Washington D.C.: Smithsonian Books, 1989, 2010)

high altitude, there were many fascinating traits about her life. Like all the women pioneers with forward thinking at least half a century ahead of her time, Amelia Earhart kept a notebook with a list of women who had accomplished leadership positions and important projects. She purposely sought a woman, Neta Snook, as her first aviation instructor, mentor, and later a friend. Amelia Earhart was the sixteenth woman in the world to receive the Federation Aeronautique Internationale license. She did not believe in higher education for women as merely the pathway to marriage and did not succumb to the pressure from society to marry. She devoted her time to be a social worker and helped people of color, and she would do anything to challenge herself to a new height, figuratively and literally. If you are a student, a resident, or a practicing surgeon, what can you do to calibrate your ceiling by taking on new challenges? Some of my colleagues go on missions to provide surgical services such as dental extractions or cleft repair. Others devote themselves to research and teaching, in addition to performing surgeries and saving lives. Many others are involved in grass-root movements and advocate for the specialty. Some write books. Leadership can start today, whether you are a student, a resident, a novice, or an experienced practicing surgeon. The sky is your limit.

While developing leadership skills as a young woman, having mentors will help to guide you toward the right direction, tapping into your inner talents and strengths. Having role models to look up to will help to envision what type of surgeon you want to become. Mentorship and coaching are extremely important throughout your career and having a sponsor can give it a huge boost. Different mentors, men or women, can help with different aspects of your personal and professional life. In the next chapter, Dr. Leslie Halpern discusses the importance of mentorship.

Leslie Halpern, MD, DDS, PhD, MPH

CHAPTER 8

A Mentor's Journey: Navigating A Paradigm Shift In Oral And Maxillofacial Surgery

by Leslie Halpern, MD, DDS, PhD, MPH, FACS, FICD

"If you are successful, it is because somewhere, sometime, someone gave you a life or an idea that started you in the right direction. Remember also that you are indebted to life until you help some less fortunate person, just as you were helped."

—MELINDA GATES

The role of mentoring in surgery and its subspecialties has a long and well celebrated heritage. The array of surgical texts regardless of specialty is abound with portraits, photos, and famous pearls of wisdom from the trailblazers who forged a path for the legacies that followed. I have been privileged as a baby boomer female to have gained knowledge from several quintessential mentors in the specialty of oral and maxillofacial surgery. Many of my contemporary colleagues and I have continued to carry the "torch of mentorship" at the pre-doctoral, residency, and junior faculty developmental levels. This commentary showcases a "journey" of surgical mentorship, beginning with historic origins, models of surgical mentoring, and the challenges faced by mentors to guide our future OMFS surgeons. A paradigm for mentorship is hypothesized that is unique to the mentee. Future directions of mentoring are presented to effectively enhance the roles of the OMFS mentor and mentee so both parties are accountable with respect to their roles and responsibilities for success.

History/Evolution Of Mentoring

The term "mentoring" has its origin within the Greek language and translates to "enduring."[65] The word "mentor" was written by Homer in *The Odyssey*. Mentor was a friend and confidant of Odysseus and was given the task of teaching and guiding Odysseus' son Telemachus. As Mentor became unable to advise, Athena took over the role disguised as Mentor and played a significant influence on the ability of Telemachus to become an adult with the wisdom and capability of leadership.

William Halstead became the true creator of a formal approach to surgical mentoring in the twentieth century. His interest in the emphasis on scientific evidence leading to clinical decisions is much of what today's surgeons follow as evidence-based practice in the clinical care of patients.[66] In the contemporary learning environment of the twenty-first century, the demographics of surgical education are changing dramatically, along with the diverse population being served. With this in mind, there is now a shift in the paradigm for surgical mentoring and this provides new innovations and opportunities for the personal and professional success of our mentees.[67 68]

---

[65] John L. Rombeau, Amy Goldberg,Catherine Loveland-Jones, eds. *"What is mentoring and who is a mentor?" Surgical Mentoring: Building Tomorrows' Leaders*. Springer Science + Business Media. (New York: Dordrecht Heidelberg, London: Springer, 2010), pp: 1-14.

[66] Rombeau, Goldberg and Loveland-Jones. *Surgical Mentoring: Building Tomorrow's Leaders*. pp:1-14

[67] Leon Assael, "Every surgeon needs mentors: A Halsteadian/Socratic model in the modern age." *JOMS* 68 (2010):1217-1218.

[68] James R. Hupp. "Two-way mentoring: Learning from residents." *JOMS* 78(2020):1-2.

Mentorship: Definitions And Dissimilarities

The literature, although abound with articles on mentorship, agrees there is no one ideal definition of mentorship.[69] The twenty-first century surgical mentor S.E. Singletary defines mentorship as a process whereby mentors are given the time and funding to develop their communication, time management, negotiation, presentation, and teaching skills. The mentor should teach by example, encourage, motivate, promote independence, and rejoice in the success of their mentees.[70] Conversely, however, mentors must be cautious, since their actions can be detrimental, i.e., taking credit on research publications without the mentee's name, as well as threatening in requests on their mentee's character and personal development. An example is rude behavior by a mentor to operating room staff in front of a resident. Negative mentoring, as such, has the potential to instill a significant lasting effect on a mentee that exceeds any positive mentoring that was experienced.[71] The latter exemplifies mentor conflict of interest that results in neglect or inadequate commitment to the relationship by either the mentor or mentee.[72][73][74]

Effective Mentors And Mentees

Mentor: The ideal mentor incorporates all of the characteristics described above. These roles, however, have become more complex and now encompass areas of work-life balance, personal development,

[69] Nuala A Healy, Peter Cantillon, Carmel Malone, and Michael J Kerin. "Role models and mentors in surgery." *Amer J Surgery* 204 (2012): 256-261.

[70] Jeremiah A. Barondess. *A brief history of mentoring.* Trans Am Clin Climatol Assoc,106 (1995):1-24.

[71] Lillian T. Eby, Jaime R. Durley, Sarah C. Evans, and Belle Rose Ragins. "Mentors' perceptions of negative mentoring experience: scale development and normological validation." *J Appl Psychol* 93 (2008):358-373.

[72] Barondess. *A brief history of mentoring.* 106:1-24.

[73] Eby, "Mentors' perceptions of negative mentoring experience: scale development and normological validation." 358-373.

[74] Singletary. *Mentoring surgeons for the 21st century.* 848-860.

and personal growth that is unique to each mentee.[75][76] Geraci et al. describes three parameters of an effective mentor: one that exhibits a degree of seniority, reputation, and experience to enhance the mentee's productivity for success; the mentor and mentee must be compatible on numerous levels with the "right chemistry" and alignment of values to ensure long-term success in their disciplines; and should not represent a supervisory position with possible conflicts of interests.[77] The dynamics of effective mentoring include active listening, emotional support, and encouragement. Mentors must be prepared for lifelong learning, educational improvement, and professional growth along with their mentee.

Mentee: Mutual respect and communication between mentor and mentee is foremost. The mentee must be proactive from the beginning to seek out a potential mentor or series of mentors. The selection is often based on expertise or academic standing, professional characteristics, and availability. The mentee is responsible for networking among peers and faculty as early as possible in their professional career. This ensures their productivity is noticed and appreciated by the potential mentor. This can also be referred to as "managing up," i.e., taking the "driver's seat" in the mentor-mentee relationship.[78] The mentee will find it advantageous to seek different mentors to address variable aspects of their professional and personal life.

Mentorship And Gender

Contemporary studies on mentorship have called for an urgent need in advancing sex and gender equity across all surgical subspecialties. The persistence of gender inequity has perpetuated

---

[75] Judy T. Zerzan, Rachel Hess, Ellen Schur, Russel S. Phillips, Nancy Rigotti. "Making the most of mentors: a guide for mentees." *Academ Med* 84(2009):140-144

[76] Jules Lin, Rishindra M. Reddy. "Teaching, mentorship, and coaching in surgical education." *Thor Surg Clin* 29 (2019):311-320

[77] Stephen A. Geraci, S. Calvin Thigpen. "A review of mentoring in academic medicine." *Am J Med Sci* 353 (2017): 151-157

[78] Esther M. Bonrath, Nicholas J. Dedy, Lauren E. Gordon and Teodor P. Grantcharov. "Comprehensive surgical coaching enhances surgical skill in the operating room: a randomized controlled trial." *Ann Surg* 262(2015):205-212.

hindrance of female advancement, research opportunities, and clinical practice.[79] Recent data in the US and UK states that although the number of women entering the field of surgery is rising, many drop out due to lifestyle preferences. Other research has argued the barriers of organization based on unfriendly work environments, gender discrimination, and "glass ceilings" prevent female surgeons rising beyond a certain level of the surgical hierarchy.[80][81][82]

Female dental and medical students, as well as residents, agree a mentor can have a significant impact on their career selection and advancement. For women identifying surgical role models, however, there exists a paucity of senior female mentors. Such underrepresentation can consequently impact the practitioner and their patient pool, i.e., research supports gender preference by female patients when compared with age-matched male cohorts.

Several solutions to these dilemmas include active recruitment of diverse teachers and developing their skills as mentors and providing mentoring strategies that incorporate cultural sensitivity to combat unconscious sex and ethnicity bias across all practitioners beginning in a pipeline fashion. Further solutions lie in mentorship roles within the work environment to encourage careers in surgery among underrepresented populations.[83] The latter affords an opportunity to embrace early interest among women and minorities, as well as provide continuous mentoring relationships whose foundation is already built during the early stages of predoctoral and resident education.

---

[79] Julie A Thompson-Burdine, Dana A.Telem, Jennifer F. Waijee, Erika A. Newman, Dawn M. Coleman et al. "Defining barriers and facilitators to advancement for women in academic surgery." *JAMA* Netw Open 2019 Aug; 2(8); e1910228, accessed December 23, 2020

[80] Mary K. Mulcahey, Brian R. Waterman, Robert Hart, Alan H. Daniels. "The role of mentoring in the development of successful orthopedic surgeons." *J Amer Acad Orthoped Surg* 26(2018):463-471

[81] A Desai, MJ. Troulis, M. August. "Evaluating the role of mentorship on women pursuing a career in oral and maxillofacial surgery." *JOMS* 78 (2020): Supplement, e 83-e 84.

[82] Megumi Himayama, Senaka Fernando. "Organizational barriers to and facilitators for female surgeons' career progression: A systematic review." *J Royal Society Med* 111(2018):324-334

[83] Bonnie S. Mason, William Ross, Gezzer Ortega, Monique C. Chambers, Michael L. Parks. "Can a strategic pipeline initiative increase the number of women and underrepresented minorities in orthopedic surgery?" *Clin Orthoped Relat Res* 474(2016):1979-1985.

Studies have focused on the gender gap with respect to the non-white woman surgeons and the lack of diversity of mentorship.[84] Frohman et al. distributed a nation-wide survey focusing on perception of salary, race, and discrimination in surgery and a lack of non-white female surgeons. Their results substantiate that there is a lack of mentors to support the challenges of race, sex, salary wage gap in women, and ability to balance work and family commitments. Larger sample sizes are needed to address the inequities of a discriminatory work environment and salary gaps across gender and whether formal mentorship programs can help navigate through these inequities. Further recruitment strategies are proposed so the number of female surgery mentors reflect the number of women pursuing surgical careers.

A systematic review by Hirayama and Fernando identified organizational barriers to the career progression of female surgeons. Organizational culture is a key barrier that forms the "glass ceiling" that hinders the progression of a woman's career. The authors propose that healthcare organizations and policymakers must support organizational facilitators that provide flexible pathways, more family-friendly working conditions, and most importantly role models and mentors in surgical specialties to change the culture of a male-dominated organization.

Mentoring Models For Gender

- Dyadic mentoring model: The dyadic model is the traditional mentoring model consisting of a one-to-one relationship and often the most successful. The dyadic approach is based on a male socialization model that consists of challenge and competition and emphasizes informational conversation over psychosocial issues.[85] This is disadvantageous to some

---

[84] Heather A Frohman, Thu-Hoai C Nguyen, Franka Co, Alexander S. Rosemurgy et al. "The non-white woman surgeon: A rare species." *J Surgical Educat* 72 (2015): 1266-1271

[85] Nanyanee Henry-Noel, Maria Bishop, Clement K. Gwede, Ekaterina Petkova, Ewa Szumacher. "Mentorship in medicine and other health professions." *J Cancer Educ*, 34(2019):629-637.

women, who are more often responsive to encouragement rather than challenge. Women also tend to engage in equalizing behavior over hierarchical behavior.

- Multiple mentoring model: This model provides the mentee with several mentors simultaneously, with each concentrating on specific areas of enhancement and growth. This model is more applicable to female mentees by providing opportunities to establish a strong network in their field of expertise.[86] The latter equalizes the hierarchy relationship, challenges, and provides encouragement for better communication.

- Peer mentoring model: This model provides collaborative approaches that are mutually beneficial among mentors, peers, and colleagues. This is advantageous to women due to their desire for equalization and willingness to collaborate, which facilitates mutual learning, support, and expression of different perspectives. Innovative work styles can be crafted to achieve the goals of mentorship. Flexibility between commitments to family and job responsibilities are better developed so females can satisfy work-life balance and advance their career aspirations.

- Mosaic mentoring: Mosaic mentoring uses multiple mentors with different types of expertise concurrent or sequentially to satisfy the changing needs of the mentee. A personalized mentor/advisor is chosen to identify and coordinate the mentee's relationships with clinical, research, and adminis-trative mentors. The advisor also guides the mentee through challenges of work-life balance. This is based on a previous decision of the mentee with respect to choosing this advisor based on respect and compatibility. This innovative approach can foster valuable steps that can expand a female mentoring pool by recruiting alumni of the program using a mosaic of

[86] Rombeau, Goldberg and Loveland-Jones. *Surgical Mentoring: Building Tomorrow's Leaders.* pg: 145-164.

vertical and peer mentoring strategies that have the potential for cultural change at the organizational level by altering the gender climate.

Mentorship And Cultural Competency

Cultural diversity is a major concern due to the increase in international students, residents, and fellows, which makes intercultural communication mandatory. In addition, the role of diversity and cultural competence in the practice of surgery will continue to grow as the ethnic composition of our patient population changes. Mentees who are culturally diverse face barriers due to the lack of identifying mentors with a similar cultural background.[87] Significant barriers include generational differences and a lack of cultural competency. As such, mentors need to be especially adept at working with and understanding cultural differences/barriers with their mentees and their patient population. This forms the basis of becoming culturally competent. Cultural competency is defined as "a set of congruent behaviors, attitudes, and policies that come together in a system, agency, or among professionals that enable effective work in cross-cultural situations."

Cultural competence must begin at the institutional level. Organizational factors, policies, and culture must remain in a dynamic state given the wide array of individuals from multiple ethnicities being trained in the US. All mentors need to be adept at working by being open to diverse perspectives, values, and experiences.[88] A study by Aggarwal et al. entitled: "Is there sex or color behind the mask and sterile blue?" examined sex and racial demographics across academic surgery by mining race and sex demographic data

---

[87] Aggarwal A, Rosen CB, Nehemiah A, Maina I, Kelz RR, Aarons CB et al. "Is there color or sex behind the mask and sterile blue? Examining sex and racial demographics within academic surgery." *Ann Surg* 2020; 273:21–27

[88] Farzenah Rostami, Anwar E. Ahmed, Al M. Best, Daniel M. Laskin. "The changing personal and professional characteristics of women in oral and maxillofacial surgery." *JOMS* 68 (2010):381-385.

for all medical students, surgical residents, and faculty extracted from the AAMC data files. The results were not surprising. Female surgery residents and faculty across all underrepresented ethnicities face unequal barriers in pursuit of these goals. These barriers are likely rooted in years of "traditional" organizational culture that promotes male domination and work-life pressure. In addition, the lack of faculty mentorship from minority women further discourages future minority women from seeing themselves in leadership roles. The authors suggest some strategies, including building pipelines across universities to recruit minority students and increase the number of minority surgical faculty and analyzing demographics over time to determine if diversity is moving in the desired direction.

Mentorship In Oral and Maxillofacial Surgery: Where Are We Headed?

A decade ago, Dr. Leon Assael stated in *JOMS* that, "Mentoring is the single most powerful tool to the learning and practice of surgery." In 2010, a survey was sent to female practicing oral and maxillofacial surgeons, as well as residents to define the changing personal and professional characteristics of women in OMFS. The results showed that since 1994 there was an increase in the number of women entering the specialty. Barriers faced included sexual harassment and a feeling of exclusion, the field still being male-dominant/ imbalanced in work/lifestyle matters, and "glass ceilings" to prevent academic advancement and leadership in educational settings.

In 2015, Dr. Danial Laskin wrote a thought-provoking editorial in *JOMS* on the role of women in academic OMFS.[89] Although with good intentions of stressing the importance of women as leaders and mentors, it failed to suggest solutions to foster a valid approach to enhance opportunities for female surgeons. There were a number of letters to the editor after Dr. Laskin's commentary argued for a lack of understanding as to the true barriers of why there are gender gaps.

---

[89] Daniel M. Laskin. "The role of women in academic oral and maxillofacial surgery." *JOMS* 2015(75): 579

Dr Mary Delsol, former president of the American Board of Oral and Maxillofacial Surgery, stated this dilemma succinctly: "The ultimate goal is to recognize surgeons—not male, female, black, white, or any other box...The critical element is that there is equal opportunity."[90]

An editorial by Dr. James Hupp provoked thoughtful arguments for how to train our future protégés (mentees) on the merits of mentoring. OMFS is a highly desirable dental specialty only attracting applicants with a combination of intellect, work ethic, compassion, and dedication to serve others. He concludes with the need to enhance diversity and inclusivity with respect to women and underrepresented minorities, especially within the organizational framework of gender fluid mentorship and leadership in OMFS.

Faculty promotion and advancement in leadership at the organizational level continue to be priorities of the mentor-mentee relationship in OMFS. Mentors should encourage female surgeons of all diverse backgrounds to seek teaching and leadership positions, integrate lifestyle, and establish long-term network relationships so they may become mentors in the future and perpetuate a better work environment for their legacy. More importantly, mentors must support the need for diversity, inclusivity, and gender fluidity to close the gaps still present at the organizational levels of academic centers. Several questions are posed:

- Why do women choose to enter academic OMFS?

- Is gender associated with success in academic OMFS?

- Is there a need to develop pipeline programs to attract applicants from all gender and cultural backgrounds to provide a future of well-rounded mentors in OMFS?

---

[90] Letters to the editor. *JOMS*, 2015, http://dx.doi.org/10.1016/j. joms2015.03.075, accessed December 24 2020.

Kolokythas and Miloro crafted the first question.[91] An online survey consisting of twenty-five questions was sent via email to all female oral and maxillofacial surgeons associated with an academic center. In the survey, surgeons were asked to name reasons for women to pursue surgery and possible pitfalls for women in career advancement. The authors received a variety of reasons for choosing academic positions, including colleagues, collaboration, teaching residents, potential for research, and not being concerned with child-rearing. Reasons for non-interest in academics included greater salary, being independent in decision-making, and more family time. Most important were the lack of female role models and the importance of mentors who can recruit more females.

Burke et al. crafted the second question.[92] There exist disparities with respect to research and academic rank between female and male oral and maxillofacial surgeons that appear uniform across other surgical subspecialties. Their hypothesis and specific aims were to determine whether there exists a similar disparity between men and women with respect to academic rank and productivity as is seen in other specialties, such as otolaryngology, ophthalmology, and plastic surgery. Their results suggested no "gender bias" with respect to research productivity or academic rank among the full-time female OMFS faculty when compared with their male cohorts. The authors do caution that future growth needs to be predicated upon shattering the "glass ceiling" with high quality mentorship of women and a continued cognizant approach to diversity to change the culture of surgical mentees and reduce gender bias. The latter will forge a path for a greater presence of female and other underrepresented groups in OMFS.

The two questions above may be proceeded by the third question: Is there a need to develop pipeline programs to attract

---

[91] Antonia Kolokythas, Michael Miloro. *Why do women choose to enter academic oral and maxillofacial surgery?* JOMS 74(2016):881-888.

[92] Andrea B. Burke, Kristie L. Cheng, Jesse T. Han, Jasjit K. Dillon, Thomas B. Dodson, Sriniva M. Susarla. *Is gender associated with success in academic oral and maxillofacial surgery?* JOMS 77(2019):240-246.

applicants from all gender and cultural backgrounds, as well as formal mentoring programs based upon diversity and gender? A study by Lee et al. examined data from dental school applicants in 2018 with respect to gender and the rise in female dental student interest in a career in OMFS.[93] Issues of a gender bias with respect to unprofessional behavior and racial-specific questions not asked of male applicants prompted a study to evaluate the interview experience between females and their male cohorts to determine factors affecting the selection of programs and ranking based upon the above assumptions. The authors concluded that although the sample was small, unprofessional behavior was more often experienced by female OMFS applicants, especially those applying to MD programs. Such discriminatory behavior characterizes an issue that needs to be carefully monitored using the standards of the Commission on Dental Accreditation (CODA) and the Accreditation Council for Graduate Medical Education (GMEC).

The implicit bias seen in the above study is a subtle enemy that needs to be eradicated by formal education of residents and faculty. Numerous toolkits and courses are available through the American Dental Education Association (ADEA) and the American Association of Medical Colleges (AAMC). Programs that are not diverse in faculty and residents may consider speaker selections for grand rounds that welcome females of all ethnicities and specialties. This will build an interprofessional collaborative of gender and ethnicity. The latter should be composed of mentors who form a mosaic of facilitators to coordinate the mentee's relationships with clinical, research, administrative duties, personality conflicts, and work-life balance.

Surgeon mentors within the specialty need to educate, elevate, and energize their residents and faculty to create a culture of diversity and gender equity. Dr. MD Fahmy in an editorial in *JOMS* states,

---

[93] Janice S. Lee, Yisi D Ji, Harvey Kushner, Leonard B. Kaban, Zachary S. Peacock. *Residency interview experiences in oral and maxillofacial surgery differ by gender and affect residency ranking.* JOMS 77 (2019):2179-2195.

"Mentorship is indeed an essential element in oral and maxillofacial surgery education."[94]

An accurate estimation on the value of mentoring should be brought to the table again with operational resources to provide rewards for mentoring at the organizational level. This will provide "protected time" to develop mentorship strategies without anxiety of lost revenue. Work-life balance and productivity can be optimized when there is no concern for loss of salary. The benefits of mentorship will ultimately help to shape the future of oral and maxillofacial surgery by perpetuating a legacy of gender equity, diversity, strength, professional development, and growth.

---

[94] Mina D. Fahmy. "Mentorship: an essential element in oral and maxillofacial surgery education." *JOMS* 77 (2019), 9-10

Relationships And Family Planning During Early Years Of Career

"Women have one advantage over men.
Throughout history they have been forced to
make adjustments."

—ELEANOR ROOSEVELT

B efore you read on, I would like to clarify that the decision to get married and have children is not the endpoint of a woman's completion. Many of us may decide to enter marriage and/or to have children, many others enjoy single life, or married life without children. This chapter is not advocating that you should get married or have children, but to give insight and feedback if you do.

You may be a student, a resident, or a fellow—single, in a relationship, engaged, or married. You may be pregnant or have just given birth. You might have a newborn, or a toddler, or more than one child. Whichever the case, before we further discuss family, I would like you to take a long, deep breath and repeat after me:

Do not focus on the notion to "have it all" or "do it all."

Instead, focus on what you think will make you happy and fulfilled at the moment, a year from now, five years from now, ten years from now, or more, and set goals to get close to it. Everyone's "all" is different. Do you envision yourself dedicated to teaching residents, doing surgeries, or doing research? Do you plan to have a family? Do you see yourself working in a private practice? Do you see yourself working part-time or full-time? Do you see yourself being a mission doctor who travels once a year to help others? What is your endpoint, or do you have one where you could say, "I think I finally have had it all"? If so, would you be happy then? What are your next steps?

Here is a picture of "having it all" for some: happily married with children, working full time with a spouse who makes good income, traveling several times a year, driving luxury cars, even owning boats or jets, living in a nice suburban neighborhood with money in the bank. Sounds pretty good. If this is your "all," then you can set goals toward that direction. But for some others, their "all" may be completely different. The problem of trying to "have it all" or "doing it all" is that this mentality inevitably leads to the imposter syndrome, because we then make ourselves feel we are not good enough, as we are constantly chasing for the "all." Everyone experiences some degree of insecurity. In small doses, it motivates you to want to be better, but as a surgeon, most of us have a type A personality. We want to be great, and we keep trying, and we have been told the definition of success by others.

Training Program Location Affects Personal Decisions In Relationships, Marriage, And Family Planning

Many female surgeons stay happily single. The decision to date, get married, or have children is entirely personal and definitely not a contest. Some might be under pressure from family, especially if your culture expects you to settle down by a certain age. Some might have gotten married and divorced and then stay happily single. Some might decide to have children while others do not.

When we are in school, pursuing residency or fellowship, where we live is dictated by where the school, residency, or fellowship program is. Obviously, the more education you pursue, the more likely you will be moving around until your thirties, and possibly into your forties. Your personal goals typically will set the priority of where you might reside. For example, if you set your goals on working as an associate professor of a particular program, you might naturally stay around that area. If you are single and the dating scene is gloomy, it might be harder to meet a potential mate. If your priority is to be near your immediate family, you might look for a job around where they are. Therefore, realistically, how far can you plan your life out? Is your personal life "on hold" until residency is completed? Are you in a relationship or married while going through residency? If so, are you getting the support you need from the residency program if you are planning to get married and start a family during residency, or are you planning to wait until you graduate? It might be a good idea to map out your current location, length of the program, and personal goals, including whether marriage or children are your priority at all.

Have *The* Conversation With Your Significant Other— More Than Once, Multiple Times, Over The Years

If you are in a serious relationship and planning the future, your spouse must understand what it requires for a spouse to be a surgeon, and you must have conversations about how this can impact your daily life. You may make a list of items for the two of you to discuss, and this list can be updated over the years as your relationship or family evolves. Here's an example of a list of important questions:

1. **Job flexibility and possible relocation:** What is the likelihood of both spouses finding jobs near the same area? If one person has to move for a better career opportunity, would the other be willing to accommodate without a great impact, including reduction in salary of one spouse?

2. **Living arrangement**: If you are in residency or just graduated, you might decide to rent an apartment after accepting your first job until you know if this position is sustainable in the long run. How long is the lease? How long are you willing to rent? Do you like living in the city, suburban area, or rural area? Do you and your spouse agree? Does one or both spouses travel often? Do you have a pet?

3. **Finances**: How are you splitting expenses? Do you have a joint account? Do you file tax jointly or separately? Do you have an accountant or financial advisor? Do you have retirement plans set up already? How about living will? If you have children, are you contributing to their college funds?

4. **Long-term career outlook**: Are you planning to work in a private practice, a teaching institution, or both? Are you working as an associate or independent contractor? If so, for how long? Are you going to become a practice owner or work for someone? If the latter, how many days do you plan to work, and when do you plan to become a practice owner? The timing may overlap with pregnancy and childbirth, which can make the beginning stage of practice building more challenging and may take longer for you to build up a practice because of the time and accommodation spent on childcare.

5. **Studying for board examination**: It is not a matter of when during your board eligibility but at what stage during your

personal life are you planning to sit for the board exams. Preparing for the board examination while you are single is the least-distracted option, speaking from experience. Pregnancy, childbirth, and raising toddlers will make board preparation harder and will require a very understanding spouse who is willing to share loads of housework. I used to work full time while pregnant, going through childbirth when preparing for the board examination. My husband would take the toddler out while I studied. My toddler scribbled all over my textbooks.

6. **Pregnancy**: Are you planning to work until you give birth? How long are you planning to take your maternity leave? If you are in a residency program, are you receiving the support you need from the program? Are you having any unforeseen issues during pregnancy that makes it more difficult for you to perform your daily tasks? Some may decide to adopt, to have a surrogate mother, or to become a single mother. No matter what decision you end up making, be sure to have a good support system around you.

7. **Childcare**: If and when you decide to have children, who will be taking care of them? If you have immediate family to help out, even temporarily after childbirth, it would be very helpful. Would your partner or spouse be actively involved with chores such as diaper-changing, or does he feel it's the women's job? Are you considering hiring a nanny or au pair, or sending your child to daycare? If so, who will pick up the child in case of sickness? If you are in the middle of surgery and cannot leave immediately, do you have backup to pick up your child? As children grow up, and enter different schools, each school has different policies. How will you juggle everything? Do you cook or do you eat out more? Do you or your spouse like to cook? Does your spouse expect hot meals on the table every day? Do you use a cleaning service? How

do you divide the house chores and is it okay to be messy sometimes?

8. **Relationship/friendship maintenance**: Are you spending quality time together and making time for date night? Are you both scrolling on your phone rather than talking to each other? Do you have friends or allies you can confide in? How often are you staying in touch?

9. **Your mental and physical health**: Being a female surgeon is a tough job. Are you eating healthy and exercising frequently? Are you taking vitamins and having routine checkups as well? Make time to do something you enjoy. Make alone time for yourself. Connect with friends. Take a hot bath. Listen to your favorite music.

A Give And Take Relationship Is Not Necessarily Always Fifty/Fifty

One chore I absolutely loathe is folding clothes. I love to cook, and I don't mind cooking fresh meals for my family every day. My husband is very neat and will fold clothes for me and wash dishes. We both don't have time to clean the house, so we hire help. You will need to decide what you like and dislike and what you can afford to hire help for so you can reserve time for your family. Outsource what you dislike and can afford to pay for. Some of my colleagues hire personal assistants or have a live-in nanny. It comes down to a balancing act between time and money. Spousal support can be extremely crucial to your career development, and how flexible your spouse is to jump in when you need to do your "surgeon thing" can make or break the relationship. My husband and I met in Manhattan during my residency. He had witnessed my calls into the ER in the middle of the night numerous times. After residency, I landed my first job in South Jersey while he still worked in Manhattan. He was very adamant that he stay there with his company, so we split the difference to commute. My husband would take care of the children when I traveled for work; he was a proud father who changed hundreds of diapers. He also cooks and cleans and he doesn't view doing chores as making him less manly. In Cheryl Sandberg's *Lean In,* she said, "Anyone who wants her mate to be a true partner must treat him as an equal—an equally capable partner."[95] It is not always possible to split duties right down the middle. One spouse might be more apt in certain tasks than the other.

Whether the female or the male in the relationship is the breadwinner, or both produce equally, you must have ongoing conversations with your partner as scenarios will change over time; what might have worked five years ago might no longer work. I used to take my children to extracurricular activities such as karate or swimming practices until too much time was taken away from my practice and I decided my children would just have to be less talented for the time being. The bottom line is, you will have to decide on who is going to be your support system, and how you will divide your time.

Being A Surgeon Mom Is Cool But Can Sometimes Be Lonely

When my eldest son was born, two other neighbor moms coincidentally had their firstborns within six months of me. I was once invited for playtime midday while I was still on maternity leave. There we were, three moms and three babies sitting in a circle, a picture-perfect moment. We had some wine and snacks, then went on to have an elaborate discussion on brands of formula, diapers, and pediatricians. I quickly ran out of things to talk about and was counting the minutes until it was over. It was my first baby playdate and my last.

There is a good chance you might be the only surgeon mom on your block. I recall not having much in common to share with neighbor moms and not being able to talk about my practice with friends. Before I started to network extensively on social media and

---

[95] Sheryl Sandberg. *Lean In.* (New York: Alfred A. Knopf, 2013) pg. 109.

in real life when my kids were little, I often found myself feeling awkward sharing baby issues with unmarried surgeon colleagues or challenges about running a practice with friends outside my profession.

In-person professional conferences are wonderful ways to meet with friends and colleagues with like minds. I look forward to returning to pre-COVID "normal" to do that again. Use the power of social media to join groups and bond with people you feel you can relate to and share some life challenges. Feeling supported and validated by people you feel comfortable with is essential to your mental health.

Self-Care And Importance Of "Me" Time

Surgeons are high-functioning professionals who are trained to take care of others first, and oftentimes taking care of our children, our spouses, and our patients can quickly deplete our physical and mental energy. It is important to block out set time on your busy schedule to decompress. It can be as simple as listening to music, watching a movie, working out, or working on a hobby. To me, something as mundane as a trip to Whole Foods makes me happy. Create a personal space where you can be undisturbed for a set period of time to recharge. Recreate happy moments by surrounding yourself with items or engaging in joyful events with loved ones. Mental health continues to be an overlooked topic; surgeons are expected to be tough and assume the roles of caregivers, so we often ignore alarming signs of burnout and stress, which often manifest as physical symptoms and psychological issues including anxiety, depression, substance abuse, and suicidal thoughts. Find your Zen and don't be alone.

CHAPTER 10

Conclusion

O ral and maxillofacial surgery is the surgical arm of dentistry, a unique specialty bridging dentistry and medicine. Dentists and physicians from World War I and World War II together repaired facial trauma; brought invasive oral and facial surgeries into a hospital setting with the aid of advancing medicine and anesthesia; created and improved residency training programs; and formed professional organizations that, over time, reflected the expanded scope of practice. Women are traditionally underrepresented in the specialty of oral and maxillofacial surgery due to factors including length of training, concerns about having children and raising a family, the atmosphere of male-dominated residency training, and discrimination and biases. Therefore, women in oral and maxillofacial surgery remain the lowest in number next to orthopedics in surgical specialties and remain lowest in number out of all dental specialties, despite the fact the Association of American Medical Colleges and American Dental Association have concurrently reached 50.5 percent female for first-year entering classes of medical and dental schools, accordingly to recent data.[96][97]

[96] Stuart Heiser. The majority of US medical students are women, New data show", AAMC.org, Association of American Medical Colleges, 02019. https://www.aamc.org/news-insights/press-releases/majority-us-medical-students-are-women-new-data-show#:~:text=Women%20comprise%20the%20majority%20of,of%20first%2Dyear%20medical%20students.(accessed Dec.9, 2019)

[97] "2018-2019" Survey of Dental Education_ Report 1: Academic Programs, Enrollment, and Graduates," Health Policy Institute, Commission on Dental Accreditation. https://www.ada.org/en/science-research/health-policy-institute/dental-statistics/education (accessed March 11, 2019)

This book is a result of my participation with the American Dental Association's Institute for Diversity in Leadership program, 2019–2020. These pages include discussions on diversity and inclusion, history of oral and maxillofacial surgery, women in dentistry and surgery, tips and strategies to prepare to be stronger candidates for residency and fellowship, mentorship, leadership, relationships, and starting a family. The bulk of this book consists of a collection of female surgeons' personal stories. This book aims to inspire more women to pursue the wonderful and fulfilling specialty of oral and maxillofacial surgery, which further enables paths to advanced fellowship such as cleft and craniofacial surgery, head and neck oncologic surgery and microvascular reconstruction, TMJ surgery, and/or translational research. Every co-contributor has a unique story. As a reader, you may be a student, a resident, or a new or seasoned surgeon. I hope there might be at least one voice from the book you can relate to and find comfort in knowing that you can do it, too, take on the journey of becoming an oral and maxillofacial surgeon. It is my hope that this book helps to illuminate your surgical career by rendering courage, knowledge, and strength every step of the way.

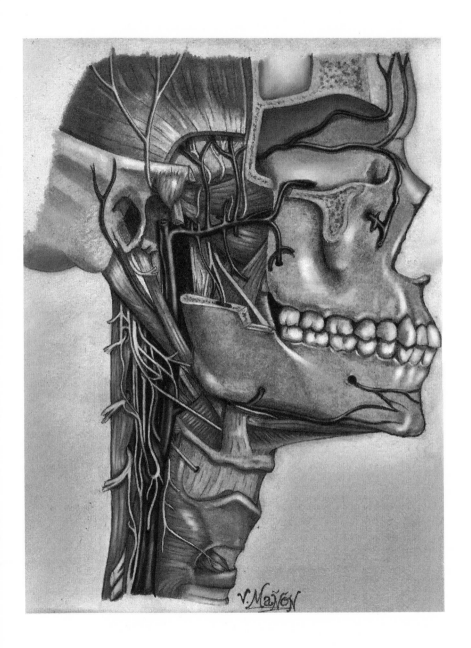

ACKNOWLEDGMENTS

I wish to thank and gratefully acknowledge the American Dental Association's Institute for Diversity in Leadership (IDL) program and all the faculty members for affording me the opportunity to create this project as part of my leadership training and development. I wish to particularly thank Ms. Susana Galvin, Senior Manager, Diversity, Equity and Inclusion, for overseeing and conducting the IDL program. Special thanks to the second VP of American Dental Association, Dr. Maria Maranga, for writing the foreword of this book. I want to thank those of my classmates from IDL who blew horns for me, in particular Dr. Sue Keller, who helped me to brainstorm on the title of the book.

I want to sincerely express my appreciation to all the co-contributors to this book: female oral and maxillofacial surgeons who dedicated their time and energy to contributing their stories. These are female surgeons across different generations who come from different backgrounds. Each story is unique, thus representing diversity within the specialty of oral and maxillofacial surgery. From October 2019 through the latter part of 2020, I reached out to different co-contributors by phone, email, or social media. I became friends with many of you. Thank you for entrusting me with your personal details, which will surely leave many people inspired.

Throughout this journey, I was able to connect with Dr. Leslie Halpern, section head of the Department of Oral and Maxillofacial Surgery at University of Utah. She was the first female resident who completed my residency program while I was the second, eight years after her. During training, I heard Dr. Halpern's name many times from the dental assistants in the clinic. She didn't know me then, but her stories had given me strength to carry on. This collaboration is especially sentimental to me. Dr. Halpern also had checked in on my progress numerous times throughout the process and offered to help on many different levels. I feel most fortunate to have her contribute a chapter on mentorship in this book—her actions of support speak volumes.

I want to express my gratitude to Dr. Rania A. Habib, an Instagram sensation with more than 10,000 followers and a leader and advocate of minority rights. Her extensive knowledge and effective personality are admirable. As a faculty member, she provides great insights on residency and fellowship applications for potential candidates. She helped to contribute two chapters in this book. Dr. Habib also helped raise funds for the production of this book through my GoFundMe campaign in the midst of COVID so I was able to reach the goal within a short period of time. Words cannot describe my appreciation of her efforts.

Special thanks to Dr. Justine Moe for allowing me to conduct an interview session on residency and fellowship applications. Thank you for your invitation for me to mention this book project at the University of Michigan Third Annual Women in OMS Leadership Symposium and to speak about coaching and sponsorship, a very important topic.

Special thanks to the amazingly talented Dr. Victoria Mañón, who created perfect imagery that captures the spirits of women oral and maxillofacial surgeons for the book cover based on my narratives of the book project. I approached her with the idea to convert photographs of female surgeons into sketches and it was a treat to see her creations firsthand. She graciously donated her time to craft all the artwork with exquisite details and lots of heart. Thank you, Dr. Chi Viet, Dr. Nicole Case Eisenberg, Dr. Rania A. Habib,

Dr. Leslie Halpern, Dr. Jaclyn Tomsic, and Dr. Justine Moe for giving me permission to use your photographs for the artwork in this book.

I want to thank all the different platforms that have offered me opportunities to speak about the topics of diversity and inclusion relating to this book project, including but not limited to OMFS Club of Columbia University College of Dental Medicine, Boston University Predental Society, University of Maryland School of Dentistry, American Association of Women Dentists, New Jersey Society of Oral and Maxillofacial Surgeons, and University of Michigan Third Women in Oral and Maxillofacial Surgery Leadership Symposium.

Special thanks to immediate past AAOMS president, Dr. Victor Nannini and VP of AAOMS, Dr. J. David Johnson, for making personal contributions toward my GoFundMe campaign, along with all the supporters of the GoFundMe campaign, whose names listed in Appendix II.

Thank you, Dr. MJ Hanlon, Dr. Shahid Aziz, Professor Julie Bencosme, Dr. Maxine Feinberg, Dr. Steven Singer, Dr. Elisa Velasquez, Dr. Suchie Chawla, Dr. Irwin Schiff, and Dr. Monica Anderson for your support of this book project. I am grateful for your friendship.

This book would not be made possible without the financial support from trade companies: Black Talon Security, Benco Dental, and Carestream Dental. Thank you for believing in my mission and supporting women's leadership.

This book is the fruit of many people's support and almost two years in the making. By putting all the stories and resources in print, we as female oral and maxillofacial surgeons make another mark in history. I hope this book is only the beginning to more publications like it and it serves to inspire more people to investigate our specialty. The world is ours.

Cathy Hung, DDS, FAAOMS, CLC
Monroe Township, New Jersey, August 2021

Resources

The Editor's Recommended Reading List

Editor's note: These are my personal favorites on various topics such as motivation, mentality, leadership, and business-building. They are not in any particular order:

Dare to Lead by Brene Brown

Braving the Wilderness by Brene Brown

See You at the Top by Zig Ziglar

Authentic Gravitas: Who Stands Out and Why by Rebecca Newton

The E-Myth Revisited by Michael E. Gerber

21 Irrefutable Laws of Leadership by John C. Maxwell

How to Win Friends and Influence People by Dale Carnegie

The 7 Habits of Highly Effective People by Stephen R. Covey

Give and Take: A Revolutionary Approach to Success by Adam Grant

Traction: Get a Grip on Your Business by Gino Wickman

Deep Work by Cal Newport

Social Chemistry: Decoding the Patterns of Human Connection by Marissa King

On Mental Toughness by Harvard Business Review

On Diversity by Harvard Business Review

On Women and Leadership by Harvard Business Review

On Public Speaking and Presenting by Harvard Business Review

Start With Why by Simon Sinek

Mindset: The New Psychology of Success by Carol Dweck, PhD

The Compound Effect by Darren Hardy

Executive Presence: The Missing Link Between Merit and Success by Sylvia Ann Hewlett

Emotional Agility: Get Unstuck, Embrace Change and Thrive in Work and Life by Susan David

The Courage to be Disliked by Ichiro Kishimi and Fumitake Koga

I Thought It Was Just Me (But It Isn't) by Brene Brown

Lean In by Sheryl Sandberg

Grit: The Power and Passion of Perseverance by Angela Duckworth

Quiet: The Power of Introverts in a World That Can't Stop Talking by Susan Cain

Leadership the Eleanor Roosevelt Way by Robin Gerber

24/7: The First Person You Must Lead Is You by Rebecca Halstead

The Extremely Busy Woman's Guide to Self-Care by Suzanne Falter-Barns

Being a Woman Surgeon: Sixty Women Share Their Stories

The Chronicles of Women in White Coats by Dr. Amber Robins and contributing authors

Women In White Coats by Olivia Campbell

The Confidence Code by Katty Kay and Claire Shipman

Navigating Your Surgical Career: The AWS Guide to Success edited by Susan E. Pories, Nancy Gantt, Christine Laronga, and Dixie Mills

The Truths We Hold: An American Journey by Kamala Harris

List Of Related Websites

American Association of Oral and Maxillofacial Surgeons (AAOMS) for dental students: https://www.aaoms.org/education-research/dental-students

American Dental Education Association (ADEA) Postdoctoral Application Support Service (PASS) application: https://www.adea.org/PASSapp/Applying/

Access OMFS blog: http://accessomfs.com/

Women In OMS Mentorship Program of the Resident Organization of American Association of Oral and Maxillofacial Surgeons (ROAAOMS): https://www.aaoms.org/education-research/dental-students/roaaoms-women-in-oms-mentorship-program

Association of Women Surgeons (AWS) resources on mentorship programs, publications, and gender equity: https://www.womensurgeons.org/page/ResourceCenter

Elaine A. Stuebner Scholars Award by American College of Oral and Maxillofacial Surgeons: https://www.acoms.org/page/Stuebner

Non-Exhaustive List Of Organizations For Oral And Maxillofacial Surgeons And Surgeons With Advanced Fellowship Training

AAOMS (American Association of Oral and Maxillofacial Surgeons)

ACOMS (American College of Oral and Maxillofacial Surgeons)

ABOMS (American Board of Oral and Maxillofacial Surgeons)

ICOMS (International College of Oral and Maxillofacial Surgeons)

ACS (American College of Surgeons)

IADR (International Association for Dental Research)

IAOO (International Academy of Oral Oncology)

AHNS (American Head and Neck Society)

AACMFS (American Academy of CranioMaxilloFacial Surgeons)

ACP (American Cleft-Palate Craniofacial Association)

AWS (Association of Women Surgeons)

GoFundMe Campaign Supporters

Background and editor's note: This book project was 100 percent fundraised through supportive trade companies, colleagues, and friends. Fundraising was made difficult during the COVID-19 shutdown, when many companies furloughed or laid off a large number of employees. Sponsorship was the last priority for many. Therefore, I decided to start a GoFundMe campaign through my social media contacts. Here are the names of the supporters of the campaign, not in any particular order. I also wish to thank those who wished to stay anonymous. Without your support, this project would not have been made possible in the midst of COVID-19.

Beatrice Leung	DeAnna Drake
Radwa Saad	Ju Yon Sophie Yi
LaJoi Wiggins	Emily Letran
Patrica Miller	Victor Nannini
Jenny Tu	Victoria Chen
Deepika Mann	Dongdan (Winnie) Guo
Sara Anderson	Farangis Farsio
Tania Nkungula	Nikole Ankrom

Brittany Eidson

Morgan Nelson

Jennifer Okhiria

Todd Hanna

Amndip Kamoh

Steve Yusupov

Delaney Islip

Trina Sengupta

Mona Stone

Lesley Robles

Rania Habib

Elisa Velasquez

James Johnson

Leslie Halpern

Pat Ricalde

Tiffany Buller-Schussler

Uyanga Jargalsaikhan

Cynthia Le

Eman Alhammadi

Suganya Appugounder

Donita Dyalram

Nora Kahenasa

Maureen Pezzementi

Janis Moriarty

Maxine Feinberg

Lisa Miller

Michele Bergen

Nicole Eisenberg

Catherine Kuo

Mary Kreitzer

Riddhi Patel

Martha Forero

Elisabeth Simpson

Trish Wen

Cassandra Stacy

Angie Rake

Heather Tuggle

Julius Case

blacktalonsecurity.com

Protecting Your Practice and Livelihood

Black Talon Security specializes in cybersecurity solutions for dental practices and secures tens of thousands of workstations across the U.S. We identify how hackers can break into your office and we work WITH your IT company to mitigate the chances of patient data theft and a ransomware attack.

Black Talon Security Proudly Supports Women OMFS

Made in the USA
Middletown, DE
12 November 2021